Ireland

CW01085291

Dominic Behan

Do Mo Cailin Ceilbhin deas o D.O'B.

Order No. AM 26725
US International Standard Book Number: 0.8256.9341.1
UK International Standard Book Number: 0.086001.760.5

Exclusive Distributors:
Music Sales Limited
8/9 Frith Street, London W1V 5TZ England
Music Sales Corporation
225 Park Avenue South, New York, NY 10003 USA
Music Sales Pty. Limited
120 Rothschild Street, Rosebery, Sydney, NSW 2018 Australia

Printed in the United States of America by
Vicks Lithograph and Printing Corporation

"A Note To Young Singers"

"TRADITION: Handing over:oral transmission from generation to generation: a tale, belief, or practice thus
handed down."
(Chamber's Twentieth Century Dictionary)

"ETHNIC: Concerning nations or races: pertaining to
gentiles or the heathen."
(Ibid)

"THE FOLLOWING I HAVE ABSTRACTED FROM MY NOTES
TO THE AMERICAN EDITION OF MY L.P. "FINNEGAN'S
WAKE.""

Historically, collectors of folk material, like Sharpe, Herd,
Ord, Child etc. have made significant contributions to the pre-
servations of folk-lore. But, to imagine - as some people would
have us believe at present - that balladry is in itself worthy of
study in an abstract art sense, is a foolish and undesirable premise.
That everything in relation to folk song must be limited to the
purely 'Ethnic', with no allowance for the day to day changes
which are a feature of any society is tantamount to asking us for
our signature on a death warrant for folk-lore. Above all, it is
asking us to sing with an academic tongue in cheek, and, before
we bawl our heads off, we must find out why. It is enough to
prevent young people from making their own songs ......

All this emphasis on 'Folk knowledge', 'Ethnic approach'
etc. is hindering the young singer. It is educating him/her into
the phony accent, the idiomatic restrictive, and the world where
song is no longer something to have on one's lips, but a kind of
mysticism related only to the professorial and ultra academic.
Forget the 'Folk pundit'. Open your mouth, and, whatever your
voice is like, sing! And to hell with the 'Ethnicists'. Folk-song
is not the special preserve of the few, but the undeniable herit-
age of the many.

DOMINIC BEHAN

NOTES ON SOME SONG MAKERS OF

THE PAST

In this collection of traditional and contemporary songs the urban may tend to outweigh the rural tradition somewhat. This is because I have deliberately tended to include only songs from the countryside written earlier than the nineteenth century. Poor, wailing songs, and songs of love, inspired chiefly by Thomas Moore's success as a 19th century court jester, are not for me. If you put your hands up to Heaven in despair at my occlusion of "Maire my Girl" or "My Mary of the Curling Hair", I can only suggest that there are plenty of recordings of this type of song made by the type of lyrical tenor likely to sing them. Nothing of Thomas Moore will be found here, indeed, I would rather busk with Harry Lauder than be got dead in the same book with him. I will, however, have a few words to say about Moore but not about what James Joyce called his "Maladies".

Geoffrey Keating was born about 1570 in Tubbrid, County Tipperary. A minister of religion, he lost his living after preaching a sermon on adultery in his native parish. It would appear that a woman, the mistress of the Lord President of Munster, who had fled to Tubbrid to escape the wrath of her husband, thought Keating's observations on chastity were addressed to her. Her lover promptly ordered his soldiers to arrest Keating. The latter, being more fleet of foot than the yeomanry, fled with manuscript and quill to the Galtee mountains and, while 'on the run', began work on "A History of Ireland" and many fine songs and poems. Keating is represented in this collection by Fintan Connolly's adaptation of the beautifully reflective "Thoughts on Inishfail", adaptation is hardly correct for the song here is really a new one, "Exiles".

John McDonnell translated the "Iliad" into Irish and it has been said that, had Pope and he been writing in the same language it would have been difficult to choose between the translations. McDonnell wrote a ballad to celebrate the visit of the Irish Queen to Elizabeth the First. There stood Grace O'Malley dressed in the garb of her country, " ... A long uncouth mantle covered her head and body; her hair was gathered on her crown and fastened with a bodkin; her breast was bare, and she had a yellow bodice and petticoat". Yet when Granu Maoil opened her mouth she was as much a Queen as Elizabeth. Her name became one more in the long list of code names the Irish were compelled by England to use when referring to their 'Green and Misty Island'.

McDonnell's "Old Erin in the Sea" has been adapted for inclusion here. He was born in 1691 and died in his native village of Charleville, County Cork in the year 1754.

When Thomas Moore was eighteen years of age he was nearly charged alongside Robert Emmett with sedition in 1798. He wrote two pieces - anonymously - for 'The Press', a highly revolutionary paper, and his Mother heard about it. She made Tom promise never again to do the likes. He kept his promise; indeed, he went further, he made a point of dedicating his translation of the "Odes of Anacreon" to the Prince of Wales.

Lord Byron said, "Tommie dearly loved a Lord", and he wasn't far out. "In society", Byron went on, "he is gentlemanly, gentle, and altogether more pleasing than any individual with whom I am acquainted".

Before Byron died, he entrusted his memoirs to Moore for posthumous publication. That Byron had given them to Moore's care as a friend no more worried Tommie than the sanctity of the songs he took from Ireland's folklore and so bowdlerised. At the behest of Lord Byron's relatives he burned the manuscripts in their presence. Emmett had been hanged drawn and quartered and his headless remains dumped, forty-nine years before Moore died peacefully in 1852.

Between studying medicine at Trinity College, Dublin, and meeting the German poet, Goethe, Charles Lever spent some time living with a tribe of Red Indians in America. He became their medicine man, and he must have been quite competent for they didn't want him to leave. Still he had to do a lot more before the Medics would allow him to practise without feathers in the British Isles, so he escaped. Back in Ireland he finished his studies in a blaze of drinkingly good fellowship.

On behalf of the poverty stricken of Dublin he fought the miserliness of the Poor Law Guardians, and that was not looked upon favourably, particularly since he happened to be one of their own dispensary doctors. In general he was not liked by the powers that were.

"Bad Luck to the Marching", his very humorous anti-war song, has been adapted for this publication. Lever was born in 1806 and died sixty-six years later.

Thomas Osborne Davis, a Protestant, joined Daniel O'Connell's Repeal Association in 1839. He soon realised however that Catholic Emancipation alone was no solution for the economic and political problems with which Ireland was then confronted. He knew his fellow Protestant Emmett had had the right idea when he said he was " ... determined on delivering my country from the yoke of a foreign and unrelenting tyranny". Or the Protestant Tone, hanged four years before the young Emmett, who fought to "break the connection with England" and bring freedom to the whole Irish race whether they be Catholic, Protestant or Dissenter.

Davis became a contributor to the revolutionary paper "The Nation" and at the same time joined the "Young Ireland" movement, a physical force organisation to which O'Connell was bitterly opposed.

Ask any schoolchild in Dublin about Davis and they'll be hard set to tell you who he was, but as they leave you, it's a safe bet they'll be singing one of his songs. Ask the same child about O'Connell and the child will maybe say, "Well, mister, I think he was some sort of a Saint like Matt Talbot".

Davis who was born in 1815 and died of consumption in 1845, is represented here by the song, "A Nation Once Again".

4

Daniel O'Connell, who was born in 1775, joined an English yeomanry corps to fight the '98 rising led by Father John Murphy, Wolfe Tone and many others. He wrote only one song which, on hearing for the first time in Cahirciveen, Kerry, I was advised by my late brother, Brendan, to forget. O'Connell died in 1847 at the height of the terrible Irish famine - in Italy.

One of the most colourful writers associated with the 'Young Ireland' movement was Charles Graham Halpine. His Father, the Rev. Nicholas Halpine, was for a time editor of the Dublin Evening Mail, a paper which ceased publication only a few years ago.

Charles took a job with the "Boston Post", and then moved on to New York to work for the "Herald", the "Times" and the "Tribune". For a short time he edited a periodical entitled, "The Carpet-Beg", and became well-known for his satire-aimed Swiftian like at the targets Upton Sinclair 'discovered' some fifty years or so later.

On the outbreak of the American Civil War, Halpine became a lieutenant on the Yankee side with the famous fighting 69th Regiment. Promoted Adjutant to General Halleck, the Southern Forces offered the sum of one thousand pounds for his capture, and further ordered that, should he or Halleck fall into the hands of their troops, they were to be shot at once.

He left the army with the rank of Brigadier-General and quickly assumed a position of importance in the Democratic Party. It was now he set about the formidable job of cleaning up the notorious Tammany Hall.

Two of his songs are remade for this collection, "Not a Star from the Flag Shall Fade", a rallying cry for the 69th., and his very humorous "Irish Astronomy". Charles Graham Halpine, born in Oldcastle, County Meath in 1829, died in America on August 3rd, 1868.

Of the other nineteenth century songmakers included here, I can really find only their songs to recommend them - which I'm sure is as it should be. "The Spinning Wheel Song" was written by John Francis Waller. "How Caeser was Driven from Ireland" is adapted from the original by John Crawford Wilson, as has been "Smith of Bristol" and "Song from the Backwoods" by Timothy Daniel Sullivan.

Woody Guthrie, the great American folksinger boasts, "My voice ain't nothin' fancy on a stick", he wants to sound like "The ash cans in the mornin', like the longshoremen bawlin'". He would therefore have been pleased to have met M.J. Moran, "(whose) gravelly, far-carrying voice ... was more notable for strength than melody".

Moran was born in Faddle Alley off Blackpitts, in what was known as the Liberties of Dublin. Two weeks after his birth in 1793 he became blind, and maybe that's how he developed the quick memory and certain retentiveness that allowed him to learn whole books from the Bible at one or two hearings. Maybe that, too, made his voice sympathetic with Moran because of his blindness, for it developed a piercing rasping quality at the top register, and a cannon boom at the bottom.

Johnny Brady had his audience at Kingsbridge, Richie Madden sang at the corner of Rutland Square, Johnny Kearney came from Wicklow to learn the trade as a blind fiddler, and the impertinent John Martin travelled up from Meath to 'elevate and instruct the music gentlemen of Dublin in the finer points of melody and refined art. How far he was capable of doing that you may judge from his favourite song, "The Muderer's Dog". But they all paled before Moran.

Down along Patrick Street and over Wintavern Street, Moran stalked each evening; his blind face to the stars and his blackthorn stick raised menacingly. His voice, accented by the gutters of Dublin, could be heard ringing across the horsehooved symphony of a city known better for its well carriaged gentry than its well fed poor. Nobody could imitate the voice of Moran and only one man ever came even near to doing so, and he was dismissed by the master in a single jeering song, "Dirty Lane".

Moran was not different to the other gleemen in voice only. His style was not the same and his repertoire depended almost entirely upon what he could make out of what he had heard. The Reverend Dr. Coyle, Bishop of Raphoe, wrote an account of Saint Mary of Egypt who was discovered doing penance in the desert by the Abbot Zozzimus, Dr. Coyle's highly theological and intellectually involved account was reduced by Moran from three hundred pages to a few verses. When the Liffey heard it for the first time, they liked it, and nobody ever referred to Michael Moran again. Zozzimus, greatest of Balladsingers had been born.

The hours from seven to nine were spent by Zozzimus at the Brazen Head tavern where he would sit in the corner, his long coat strealing the floor, and his beaver hat nodding attentively in the direction of the voice of Dickie McGrane who read the news of the day for his master. Then, with fragments of news becoming versified in his mind, he stamped his way to the Carlisle Bridge where he silenced the most unruly audience with thunderous abuse. He would interrupt himself to straighten the scansion but from his customers he brooked no interference.

The Winter of 1854 proved too hard for even the great Zozzimus and he set about composing his own funeral march, "In the O'Connell Circle let me be", and he admonished the mourning gleemen of Dublin who surrounded his death bed to make his funeral simple, "All pomp is vain, illustrious people does prefer it plain". Before Zozzimus died, Dickie McGrane brought him news of the death of his great rival Mary Webb, Big Mary of the Coombe, "Mrs. Webb" he whispered, the great voice gone, "for the first time yeh got ahead of me but I won't be long catchin' yeh up".

The late Philip Rooney deals with what took place soon after the death of Zozzimus, " . . . . . For a time it seemed that the spirit of Zozzimus was not at rest . . on a twilight evening soon after his death, there came out of the Liberties a terrifyingly familiar figure . . . face uplifted blindly to the sky, cape coat bundled about . . . tall gaunt ,,, into the dusk rang the lined that the Liffeyside knew so well, "If yis want wit and fun, to me, Zozzimus come, for I am the boy your hope and your joy to en-liven yer souls!" It was almost the voice of Zozzimus, but not quite, the unique quality which had made Michael Moran what he was, was subtly missing. Not all his mimicry . . . not even his cunning copy of the beaver hat and scalloped coat could make Dickie McGrane succeed in the plan which he had been hatching . . . through all the years of his servile friendship . . The shoes of Zozzimus were too big for any imitator to fill. Dublin had loved the real article too well to be deceived by the counterfeit.

6

CONTENTS

CONTENTS

(Continued)

A BRAVE NEW WORLD

Words & music by Dominic Behan

Tell me now that hate lies sleep-ing, Tell me now the flag is - furled, Sing to me an end to weep-ing Bring to me vi-sions of a brave new world. Tell me now the day has dawned love, That man to man a love as - strong has stirred. Sing with me, Sing loud this song love, Sing a great wel-come to a brave new world.

2. Tell me now that hate is dying, tell me now the war flag will fade,
Tell me now that man is trying to use for man's greatness what great man has made,
To raise aloft from degradation creating great and glorious deeds by the word,
The word is love for countless nations countless men working for a brave new world.

3. Tell me now that hate is dead love, tell me now the flag is done,
Tell me how there is instead love, in all our hearts hostility for hatred's wrongs.
When you sing for me this song, love, to lull the earth our Mother long disturbed,
Only then can we be one love where our children live laughing in a brave new world.

2 AN RAIB TU AG AN gCARRAIG?
(WERE YOU AT THE ROCK?)

Translated from the Irish, freely, by Fintan Connolly.

Did you go then to — the grey rocks, And be-hind a — wind-swept cre - vice there ———— Did you find our Ma -ry— gent- ly wait - ing, Our —— La -dy, sweet and fair? —— Did the sun shine bright - ly —— 'round Her Ma -king gold darts through— her —— hair? —— And will you stay si - lent as the day —— When the wind has left the air? ——

2.   Oh, my Mary, long we wait here
      While the hunter combs the mountains high,
      And the soft wind whispers "Guard Her,"
      'Though as hunted we must die.
      Oh, the dawn is longtime coming,
      And the long night clings with care,
      But they shall not find with their chains to bind
      My Mary, pure and fair.

A NATION ONCE AGAIN

By Thomas Osborne Davis

When boy-hood's-fire was in my-blood I read of an-cient- free-men, For Greece and - Rome who - brave - ly stood three hun - dred men - and - three men And then I - prayed I yet might see our fet - ters rent in twain, And - Ire-land long a pro-vince be a na - tion once a - gain. A na - tion once a - gain, A na-tion once a - gain, And Ire - land - long a pro - vince be a - na - tion once a - gain.

2.   And from that time through wildest woe that hope has shone a far light,
Nor could love's brightest Summer glow outshine that solemn starlight,
It seemed to watch above my head through forum field and fane,
Its angel voice sang round my bed a nation once again!
Chorus:

3.   So, as I grow from boy to man I bent to me that bidding,
My spirit of each selfish plan and cruel passion ridding,
For, thus I hoped some day to aid, nor can such hope be vain,
When my dear country shall be made a nation once again.
Chorus:

4

A POUND FOR TO LEND

Words by Charles Joseph Kickham re-arranged and music remade by D. Behan

Verse.

I've a pound for to lend. I've a pound for to spend, And 'cead mi-le fail-te' is me word for a friend. No mor-tal I en-vy. No mas-ter I own, or lord in his cas-tle, or king on his throne. He's the king of good fel-lows, the poor hon-est man, So let's drink and be mer-ry as long as we can. We'll che-rish their fame, boys, who died long a-go, And what's that to the Sas-en-ach whe-ther or no!

Chorus.

Whe-ther or no, Whe-ther or no. What's that to the Sas-en-ach, Whe-ther or no!

2. The spinning wheel stops and the girls grow pale
While their Mother is telling some sorrowful tale
Of a snug cabin levelled or coffinless graves
Or ships swallowed up by the salt ocean waves,
But our three gallant boys on parade they are seen
In the ranks of the brave 'neath the banners of green
We've taught them to guard it 'gainst traitor and foe
And what's that to the Sassenach whether or no.
Chorus:

3. Come here bean na tighe* sit beside me a while,
By the light in your eye let me read in your smile
Would you give your old home for the lordliest hall?
Ah! You glance at my rifle that hangs on the wall!
Come fill up all neighbours, fill high to the brim,
And cry slainte* to freedom again and again.
May traitors and treason keep far from our door
And may we live in plenty and peace evermore.
Chorus:

*1. Cead mile failte: A hundred thousand welcomes. Pronounced: Cayd meela faulta.

*2. Bean na tighe: Woman of the house. Pronounced: Bann nah tee.

*3. Slainte: Health! Pronounced: Slauntyeh

A pound for to lend 2

5

AS I WAS GOING O'ER THE MOOR

Arranged and adapted with new words by Fintan Connolly

It's cold and raw the north wind blows black in the morn-ing ear-ly, - When all the hills are co-vered in snow 'Tis then 'tis win-ter sure-ly. - As I was go-ing o'er the moor I met a far-mer's daugh-ter,- Her cher-ry cheeks and sloe black eyes they caused my heart to fal-ter. -

2. I bowed to greet her very low, to let her know my meaning,
    She answered with a radiant smile, her looks were very pleasing,
    "Where are you goin' my pretty girl, now in the morning early?"
    Below her eyes she answered "Well, kind sir, to sell my barley."

3. "Now I've guineas here for you and twenty more that's yearly,
    "Don't go to town I'll pay what's due and I'll buy all your barley,
    "If twenty guineas would win the heart of the girl I love so dearly,
    "All for to stay with me tonight and go home in the morning early?"

4. As I was going o'er the moor the very morning after,
    Who should I meet upon the way but the farmer's lovely daughter,
    And though the day was cold and wild, with her I thought to tarry,
    But she passed me with a fleeting smile, "Kind sir, I've sold me barley."

BAD LUCK TO THE MARCHING

Arranged and adapted by Dominic Behan from the original by Charles Lever

Bad luck to the march-ing, pipe-play-ing and starch-ing, How neat it must be to be killed by the French. I'm sick of pa-ra-ding, through wet and cold wa-ding, or stand-ing all night to be shot in a trench.

2.   To the tune of a fife they'll dispose of your life,
You surrender your soul to some elegant lilt,
Now I like Garryowen when I hear it at home,
But it doesn't sound sweet when you're going to be kilt.

3.   Like a sailor that's nigh land I long for that island,
Where drinking's the order and hour if you please,
Where it is no disgrace if you don't wash your face
And you've nothing to do but just stand at your ease.

4.   With no sergeant to abuse us we fight to amuse us,
Sure much better beat Christians than kick a baboon,
Oh I'd dance like a fairy to see ould Dunleary,
And think twice e'er I'd leave it to be a dragoon.

7

THE BALLAD
OF OLIVER St. JOHN GOGARTY

Words and Music adapted by Dominic Behan from the original by Mr. Dawson of Dublin

Come all you brave free stat - ers now And lis - ten to my say, —— For lord's sake pay - at - ten -tion —— to what I have to say, —— For it is the tale of a win - ter's night one Ja - nu - a - ry year When - O -li – ver St. John - Go - gar - ty swam down to the sal -mon weir.——

2. As Surgeon St. John Gogarty one night sat in his home
    A-writing of prescrip-ti-ons, or composing of a poem,
    Up rolled a gorgeous Rolls Royce car, and out a lady jumped,
    And at Oliver St. John Gogarty's hall-door she loudly thumped.

3. As Oliver St. John Gogarty inside the lady led
    A couple of masked ruffians put guns up to his head.
    Thay drove him to a house in Islandbridge and locked him in a room,
    And said "Oliver St. John Gogarty, prepare to meet yer doom! "

4.   Said Oliver St. John Gogarty, "My coat I beg you hold".
       The half-bemoidered ruffian than did as he was told.
       Before he twigged what game was up the coat was round his head,
       And Oliver St. John Gogarty into the Liffey fled.

5.   The Oliver St. John Gogarty hypocratically he swore
       That if the Gods decreed that he should reach the other shore
       By the blessed martyr Oliver and by the two Saint Johns
       He'd present the bloody Liffey with a pair of mated swans.

6.   While passing through the Phoenix Park a polisman he passed by,
       Cried Oliver St. John Gogarty, "A senator am I,
       "The rebels I've tricked, the river I've swum", said the polis with a wink,
       "Ah sure Oliver Senator Gogarty, you've too much bounce to sink."

7.   He gave the Liffey the grandest swans that ever swam a brook,
       But Jemmy Joyce answered the man inside a bloody book,
       "Oh God", cried Oliver Gogarty, "I'd rather end me days
       "In swimming the Liffey with me swans than a hero in 'Ulysses'".

Oliver St. John Gogarty 2

8
THE BONNY BUNCH OF ROSES

Arranged and adapted by Dominic Behan

Near the cor-ner-of the o-cean-one plea-sant eve-ning in the month of June When-all the-fea-thered-song-sters their li-quid notes did sweet-ly tune It was there I saw a-fe-male-and on her-face there was a sign of woe Con-ver-sin'-with young Bo-na-parte con-cern-ing the Bon-ny Bunch of Ro-ses O.

2.   Then up spoke young Napoleon and takes his Mother by the hand,
    Saying "Mother dear be patient until I'm able to command
    "I'll raise a mighty army and through tremendous dangers go,
    "And I never will return again until I've conquered the Bonny Bunch of Roses O".

3.   "Oh son, be not too venturesome for England is the heart of oak
"And England Ireland and Scotland their unity shall ne'er be broke,
"Remember your dear Father in Saint Helena he lies low,
"And of you follow after beware the Bonny Bunch of Roses O".

4.   "When first you saw great Bonaparte you fell upon your bended knees,
"You asked your Father's life of him, he granted it right manfully,
"It was then he took his army and over the frozen Alps did go,
"And he swore to conquer Moscow and return for the Bonny Bunch of Roses O".

5.   "He took three hundred thousand men and kings likewise to bear his train,
"They were so well provided for that he could rob the worlds for gain,
"But when he came to Moscow he was defeated by the frost and snow,
"And with Moscow all a-blazing he lost the Bonny Bunch of Roses O".

6.   "Oh Mother dear it is now adieu for I lie here on my dying bed,
"Had I lived would I have been clever? But now I droop my youthful head,
"Yet when my bones are mouldering and weeping willows o'er me blow,
"The name of Napoleon Bonaparte will enshrine the Bonny Bunch of Roses O".

The Bonny Bunch Of Roses 2

9

BOOLAVOGUE

Arranged and adapted from the original of Myles Byrne by Wolfe Stephens

Come all you war-ri-ors and re-nowned no-bels give ear un-
to my - war-like theme, And I will tell you how fa-ther Mur-phy late-ly a-
roused from his sleep-y dream For Ju-lius Cae - sar nor A - lex-
an - der nor yet King Ar - thur could e-qual him arm - ies for-
mid - a - ble He did con-quer through with two gun men he did be - gin.

2. When Enniscorthy was subjected by him 't'was next to Wexford we marched our men,
    And on the Three Rock took up our quarters waiting for the daylight the town to win,
    At Carraig Rua some time we waited and next to Gorey we did repair,
    At Tubberneering we thought no harm but the bloody army was waiting there.

3. The issue of it was a close engagement and on the soldiers we spared no thanks,
    Through bushes marshland and shady thickets there were mangled bodies and broken
                                                                              ranks,
    The British Fencibles I'll not forget them they soon got the brushes on their helmets
                                                                              straight,
    They turned around and they charged for Dublin as though engaged in a huntin' chase.

4. Some crossed Donnybrook and more through Blackrock and others up Shankhill without
                                                                              wound or flaw,
    But if Barry Lawless is not a liar there's more went groaning up Luggelaw.
    May God attend you brave Father Murphy yeh fought the battle as best yeh knew,
    And though yeh told us to give up our arms it's in yer fightin' we'll think of you.

Enniscorthy, The Tree Rock mountain, Carraig Rua, and Tubberneering and Luggelaw are
places in County Wexford.

Donnybrook, Blackrock and Shankhill are towns around County Dublin.

THE BOY FROM WEXFORD

Words and music remade by Dominic Behan

It was ear-ly ear-ly all in the Spring The birds did whis-tle and sweet-ly sing Chan-ging their notes from tree to tree And the song they sang – was old Ire-land free.

2. 'Twas in the darkest hour of night
    The Yeoman cavalry gave me a fright
    The Yeoman cavalry was my downfall
    And a prisoner I was taken by Lord Cornwall.

3. 'Twas in the guard-house where I was laid,
    And in the guard-house was I tried,
    My sentence passed by the Saxon foe
    And to Dungannon I was forced to go.

4. As I was dragged along Wexford Street
    My own first cousin I chanced to meet,
    My own first cousin did me betray
    For one bare guinea swore my life away.

5. My sister Mary in great distress
    Ran down the stairs in her cold night dress,
    My life my virtue I will lay down
    To see my brother safe in Wexford Town.

6. As I was stood on the gallows high,
    Who but my Father was standing by,
    My Father stood and did me deny
    And the name he gave me was the Croppy Boy.

7. In Dungannon my corpse will lie,
    For in Dungannon I must die,
    Don't shed a tear as you pass by,
    For I go proudly as the Croppy Boy.

11

THE BOSS ALAS

Words by Fintan Connolly, tune adapted

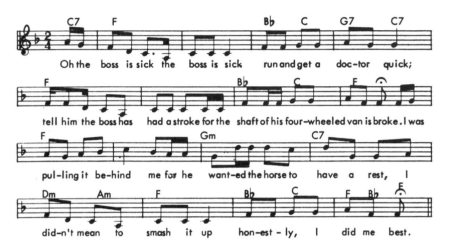

Oh the boss is sick the boss is sick run and get a doc-tor quick;

tell him the boss has had a stroke for the shaft of his four-wheeled van is broke. I was

pul-ling it be-hind me for he want-ed the horse to have a rest, I

did-n't mean to smash it up hon-est - ly, I did me best.

2. Oh the boss is dead, the boss is dead,
   They've laid a tombstone on his head
   Some say it's to praise what he was about,
   But I'm sure it's to stop him getting out.
   For years and years I've waited
   To see this most respected soul
   In a place where he for years kept me,
   Down a great big dirty hole.

3. May the worms crawl in and out of him,
   The filthy rotten faggot man,
   May his flesh they leave like a well-drilled cheese
   Under a ganger maggot-man
   May his money turn to rust
   And the guts of his body run to dust,
   And when I next see that hard hearted rock
   May he be part of a concrete block.

4. Just one more prayer in the boss's ear,
   I'm going to louse around all day,
   At the slightest chance I'll start to dance,
   And you can't stop me for you're wrapped in clay,
   But if by some sheer miracle
   To heaven they take your mangled wreck
   I hope you run into a space machine
   And break your dirty rotten neck.

BRIAN O'LYNN

12

Arranged and adapted with new music by Wolfe Stephens

Now - Bri - an O' Lynn had no hat to put on so he went to a neigh-bour to - bor - row a one, There was none of the crown left and less of the brim "Tis a fine ven - ti - la - tion" said Bri-an O' Flynn.

2.   Brian O'Lynn had no shirt to his back
So he went ot a neighbour and borrowed a sack.
He cut a place for his arms and a place for his chin,
"'Tis like linen itself" said Brian O'Lynn.

3.   Now Brian O'Lynn round his chest hed no coat,
So he stripped off the skin of a neighbouring goat,
He put the fleshy side out and the woolly side in,
"'Twill be the last word in fashion" said Brian O'Lynn.

4.   Now Brian O'Lynn to his house had no door,
He'd the sky for a roof and the bog for a floor,
He had a way to jump out and a way to jump in,
"'Tis a fine habitation" said Brian O'Lynn.

5.   Now Brian O'Lynn went a-courting one night
So he said both the Mother and daughter to fight,
To fight for his hand they both stripped to the skin,
"Sure I'll marry yeh both" said Brian O'Lynn.

6.   Now Brian O'Lynn and the daughter and Mother
Were all lyin' close in the bed together,
The night it was cold and the blankets were thin,
"Lie close to the wall", said Brian O'Lynn.

7.   Brian O'Lynn with the wife and Mother
All went over the Bridge together,
The bridge it broke down and they all tumbled in,
"Sure we'll go home be water", said Brian O'Lynn.

13

THE BROWN AND YELLOW ALE

Translated from the Irish by James Stephens
Arranged and adapted with new music by Dominic Behan.

2.   He asked me if the woman by me side was me daughter
     Oh the brown and the yellow ale,
     When I said she was my wife his manner didn't alter,
     Oh oh, love of my heart.

3.   He asked me if I'd lend her for an hour and a day,
     Oh the brown and the yellow ale,
     I said if yeh think it's fair then take her away,
     Oh oh, love of my heart.

4.   He said then you take the high road and I'll take the upper,
     Oh the brown and the yellow ale,
     And we'll meet again by the ford of the river,
     Oh oh, love of my heart.

5. I was waiting by the ford for an hour and three-quarters,
   Oh the brown and the yellow ale,
   When she came to me 't'was without shame I saw her,
   Oh oh, love of my heart.

6. When she told me her story I lay down and I died,
   Oh the brown and the yellow ale,
   She sent two men for timber and she never even cried,
   Oh oh, love of my heart.

7. A board of alder and a board of holly,
   Oh the brown and the yellow ale,
   And two great yards of sack about me,
   Oh oh, love of my heart.

8. Now had my own little Mother never been a woman,
   Oh the brown and the yellow ale,
   I'd sing you many another song about women,
   Oh oh, love of my heart.

The brown and the Yellow ale 2

14
THE BUTCHER OF GLOUCESTER D

New music and words by Wolfe Stephens

There lived a butch-er once a time down in the Glou-cester Dia -mond, His
sec-ond name was Bel - i - cose his first wan it was Si - mon, He
loved a mot from Fran-cis street and ea - ger-ly he sought her, But her
fath - er would-n't let them meet for he lived a-cross the wa - ter.

CHORUS

Oh - and aye - a butch-er he was a de - mon, The
girl's fath - er fanc-ied Shels the butch-er liked Bo - hem-ians - If
she mixed up the foot - ball shirts he nev - er would for - give her, - Take
back your heart by north-side man me girl was reared on liv - er. -

2.   From Batchelor's walk to Eden quay a no man's land was cited,
      And neither one could cross the way unless they were invited,
      So every evening when the hand was ten right on the jiffey,
      The people gathered round in bands to shout across the Liffey.
      Chorus:

3.   The girl and victualler grew very tired of meeting,
      For him to shout across at her and she return his greeting,
      So they made a daring plan to kill the girl's Father,
      But a darin' plan for any man he must get across the water.
      Chorus:

4   He hurled abuse across the stream and then rode over on it,
      A curse or two he had to spare so they both rode home upon it,
      And in a bed on Francis Street he saw a face unshaven,
      He took the knife he had for meat and soon the life had taken.
      Chorus:

5.   There me story it must end I'm sorry it wasn't shorter,
      But if you add a verse or bend the chorus make it longer,
      The man who lay down in the bed was not Father to the daughter,
      It's a decent child who knows the head of a family 'cross the water.
      Chorus:

The Butcher of Gloucester D. 2

15
THE BROWN THORN BUSH

Translated from the Gaelic by Wolfe Stephens, music remade.

Oh if I were but a skill-full sai - lor it's - ov - er the sea I'd
run And - a few short lines - from my pen - to - my
dear - est - sweet-est one And - when no more the fin -
est - wo - man in the land I can eas-'ly claim I would
stay a-way from life and lov - in' for I would - have lost the game

2. "And now", she'd say, "that you have gone, safely you may return
    "You've killed the heart within my breast my soul with anguish burns,
    "And I have no gold to send my love nor even a small boat to bring to him,
    "And the sea in flood between us and I not able to sail or swim.

3. "My Father he is in the clay and my Mother her heart a stone,
    "And the young men of Ireland angry with me and my love away from home.
    "Greatly was he deceived in not thinking my thought in love aright,
    May he not return till I am married - married and well out of sight.

4. "A foolish man it is who would climb to the top of the highest fence,
    "While a smaller one's beside the first and where I could count my pence,
    "Though the brown thorn bush be tall it is bitter on high you can see,
    "And the sweetest of fruit shall flower down below on the lowest tree".

CARRICROE

Words by Dominic Behan,

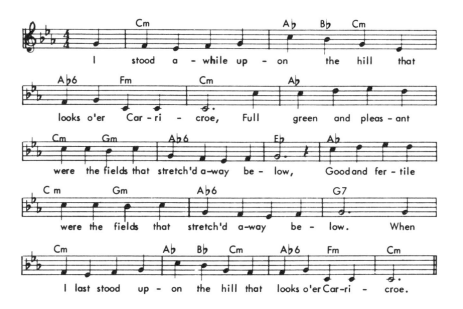

2.   The hill was splendid in the sun that shone on Carricroe,
       But cold upon the famine fields that stretched away below,
       Like ice it shone upon the famine fields that stretched below,
       Then dark the crest upon the hill that looks o'er Carricroe.

3.   I stood upon that dreadful hill that looks o'er Carricroe,
       That awful headstone standing o'er the famine fields below,
       Neglected are the famine graves that stretch away below,
       And dark the famine headstone that looks o'er Carricroe.

17
THE CASTLE OF DRUMBOE

Words and music remade by Dominic Behan

The mid-night hags are shriek-ing round the cast-le of Drum-boe While – pat-riot blood-is flow-ing red in the sod-den soil be-low, Their –crime, that they-had left their homes to fight a fo-reign foe, And by I-rish hands they were mur-der'd in the cas-tle of Drum-boe.

2. From Cork and Kerry homes they came, from Munster green and fair,
   To fight the blood-stained Black and Tans and dare what men will dare,
   Black treachery betrayed them, informers wrought their woe,
   Oh! Ireland you have murdered them in the Castle of Drumboe.

3. You have sold the pass for England's gold. Sold many the pass and gorge,
   You have cringed to Orange Carson and knelt to English George,
   Even borrowed English armoury your country to overthrow,
   And you've murdered Ireland's fighting men in the Castle of Drumboe.

CHILD WEDDING

Arranged and adapted by Dominic Behan

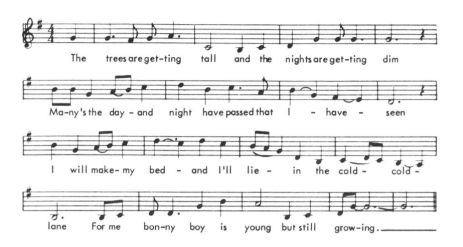

The trees are get-ting tall and the nights are get-ting dim
Ma-ny's the day - and night have passed that I - have - seen
I will make- my bed - and I'll lie - in the cold - cold -
lane For me bon-ny boy is young but still grow-ing.

2. Oh Father dearest Father you've done me very wrong,
    For you have married me to a boy that's far too young,
    He is hardly fifteen years and I'm gone twenty-one,
    And me bonny boy is young and still growing.

3. Oh daughter dearest child sure I've done yeh no wrong
    For I have married you to a local farmer's son
    He will be the man and you will be his queen
    Though yer bonny boy is young yet he's growing.

4. Then Father dearest Father I'll tell yeh what we'll do
    We'll trim for him a bonnet that's rimmed all round with blue
    And we shall place it easily around his forehead true
    For to let the people know that we're married.

5. As I walked down one evening all by the College wall
    I saw me own young boy and he was playin' at the ball,
    I looked at him from high above he didn't hear me call
    'Tis a sad day a boy stops his growing.

6. At the age of fifteen years he was a married man
    And when he was seventeen he'd gotten me a son
    At the age of eighteen years the grass it grew green over him
    Cruel death had put an end to his growing.

19

CHEER UP! RUSSELL STREET

Children's street song, new arrangement by Dominic Behan

Cheer up Rus-sell Street it's known - ev - 'ry - where We knocked down Em - met Street and left him ly-ing there, He called for mer - cy but mer - cy was-n't there, Cheer up Rus-sell Street it's known ev - 'ry - where.

CHORUS

It's a rare oul street to play for _____ it's a rare oul street to know _____ When - you read - a - bout our his-tor - y It's e - nough to make your

heart grow sad, sad, sad, sad, We don't care whe-ther we

win lose or draw - for all - the hell we care

All - we know - there's goin' to be a row - and

good oul - Rus-sell - er will be there.

2. When we went out to Phoenix Park our team was Bendigo,

    Railway Celtic were with us and Ash Street was the foe,

    They'd razor blades and bicycle chains to bate us from the field,

    But the Southside men thought twice again when they met the Northside breed.

    Chorus:

Cheer up! Russell Street 2

33

20
COME ALL YOU BRAVE UNITED MEN

Arranged and adapted with new music by Wolfe Stephens.

Come all you brave u-nit-ed men who would right- your coun-try's wrong, I'll sing to you a verse or two which won't - de - tain you long. In old Ive - lea-ry by the hills my youth - ful days passed by, The fa - mine came and filled the graves, I saw - my fa - ther die.

2. The bailiff with the notice came the bit of ground was gone.
I saw the whole roof in a flame when the crowbar work was done.
With neither house nor bed nor bread the Workhouse was my doom
And on my jacket soon I read, "The Union of Macroom".

3. My Mother died of a broken heart my uncle from the town
Brought for her a horse and cart, and buried her in Gleown,
I joined the redcoats then, Mo Leir* what would my Father say?
And I was sent in one short year on service to Bombay.

4. I thought to be a pauper was the greatest human curse,
But serving in a robber's cause I found it ten times worse,
I helped to plunder and enslave the tribes of India's sons,
And I spent many a sultry day blowing Sepoys from our guns.

*   Mo Leir - My grief.

5. I told those sins to Father Ned, the murder and robbery,
    "They are not sins for you" he said, "you only did your duty".
    And when that duty here was done, the journey home I made,
    To find my friends all dead and gone, so I joined the Pope's Brigade.

6. They pinned some medals on my breast for serving the Pope's campaign,
    And then I went to the far far West a soldiering again,
    Then with the famous Captain Billy Byrne II joined the Fenian band
    Resolved to strike another blow to free oul Ireland.

7. Back in my downtrod Isle again where vultures drink our blood,
    Friends are scattered starved and slain, some say I am cursed by God,
    That I could swear my love long day to serve from Pole to Pole,
    In any other cause but this with safety to my soul.

8. It's no sin to kill for England's greed in some far foreign clime,
    How can it be that love for you my Ireland is a crime?
    Why should we be by Pope's decree scourged, outlawed and banned,
    Because we swore one day to free my trampled native land?

Come all you brave united men   2

21 THE CONNAUGHT RANGERS

Words and music by Wolfe Stephens

All in the morn-ing when the day was dawn-ing They took him down in-to the grim dark - square And there they shot him and soon for-got him For a sol-dier reck'd no wor-ry be he here nor there, "Aim for my heart" lads he cried - un - to them - "For this your ma - jes-ty - pays ten shil-lings each day, "May God for-give you-" His ges-ture threw them - then he brave-ly stood and died the sold-ier's on - ly way.

2.   The sun was burning when home returning,
       Through Indian street they walked so far from their God,
       No man spoke to them for all who knew them
       Said "They are the riflemen of Daly's firing squad,"
       "We had our orders we had to just obey them,
       "How can we but refuse our Colonel's rightful command?"
       But men turned from them for there upon them,
       Was the blood of Ireland's hero shot in India's land.

   But we salute him and pay tribute to him,
       We'll put his name before us now in letters of gold,
       For Ireland's winning we're just beginning,
       And the Empire that destroyed you is growing old.
       Each freeborn nation is Daly's salvation,
       Each country free is another link gone
       In the chain that bound men to kill and hound men,
       For a diamond in the blood red setting of the English crown.

In 1916 Lance Corporal Daly was executed in India following a mutiny by Connaught
Rangers on hearing of the execution of the 1916 leaders.

CROOKED JACK

22

Words and tune adapted by Wolfe Stephens.

Come I-rish men both young and stern with ad-ven-ture-in-your soul There are o-ther ways to spend your days than work-ing-down a hole I was tall and true - all of six feet two till they broke me a-cross the back. By a name I'm known that's not my own for they call me - crook-ed Jack.

2. The ganger's blue eyed pet I was,
   Big Jack could do no wrong,
   And the reason simply was because
   I could work hard hours and long.
   Chorus:

3. I saw men old before their time,
   Their faces drawn and grey,
   I never thought so soon would mine
   Be lined the selfsame way.
   Chorus:

4. I cursed the day I went away
   To work on the hydro' dams,
   Our sweat and tears, our hopes and fears
   Bound up in shuttering jamms.
   Chorus:

5. They'll say that honest toil is good
   For the spirit and the soul,
   But believe me boys it's for sweat and blood
   They want you down that hole.
   Chorus:

23

DICEY RILEY

Street song adapted with new music and words by Dominic Behan

2.   She'll walk along Fitzgibbon Street with an independent air,
Then it's down by Summerhill and see the people stare,
She'll say it's nearly half past one so I'll go in for another one,
For the heart of the roll is Dicey Riley.

3.   Long years ago when men were men and fancied May Oblong,
Or lovely Becky Cooper or Maggie Mary Wong,
One woman put them all to shame just one was worthy of the name
And the name of that same was Dicey Riley.

4.   But time went catchin' up on her like many pretty whores,
It's after yeh along the street before yer out the door,
The balance weighed their looks all fade but out of all that great brigade
Still the heart of the roll is Dicey Riley.

*Pop : slang term for pawn office.

© Copyright 1965, CODA MUSIC LIMITED,

DIRTY LANE

New words and music by Wolfe Stephens

At the dir - ty end of - Dir - ty Lane lived a
dir - ty cobb - ler called Dick Mc - Grane His- wife she was in the
oul Queen's reign A - stout brave o -range wo-man o' She was a bi - got
like her clan and in the streets she loud-ly ran, With her ro - ly to - by
ro - ly ran and yer oul jade wife on the town - o.

2. For twenty years or maybe more oul Dick lived with this dirty great big boor,
Well matched were they to rob the poor and steal from blind men's boxes O.
On Essex Bridge she sprained her throat and six a penny was her note,
Oul Dickie wore a brand new coat she got from livin' with the Yeoman O.

3. Now everyone knows my singing pitch on Carlisle Bridge was robbed by this oul bitch,
With oul Dickie she planned a cute oul switch to defraud my loyal patrons O.
But quality will always tell no man the sham can ever sell especially
When his voice was made in Hell and hers as far from Heaven O.

4. If yeh steal me purse yeh do me no wrong but God forbid yeh should ever rob me
songs,
For it's down in Hell such likes belongs and not with decent people O.
Forgive them all the Bible says who trespass you in every ways,
But I'm sure they never meant McGrane and his oul jade wife on the town O.

25
DOWN IN YONDER MEADOW

Children's street song arranged and adapted by Dominic Behan

2: Mary made a dumpling she made it so sweet she cut it up in slices
And gave us all a piece,
Saying, "Take this, Don't say no, for tomorrow is my wedding day,
And I must go".

THE DUBLIN FUSILIERS 26

New words and music by Wolfe Stephens.

Now if yer oul fel-la is out of work and na-tion-al-i-ty Let him join up to fight the Turks or keep poor Bel-gium free And if there is no room out there let him go on the beer At twen-ty two and six a week with the Dub-lin Fu-si-liers.

CHOS.

With yer left right, right a-bout turn, This is the way we go, March-in' with fixed bay-'nets, the ter-ror of ev-'ry foe, cre-dit to the na-tion ten thou-sand buc-can-eers And a ter-ror to cre-a-tion are the Du-b-lin Fu-si-liers!

2. Bold Hindenberg looked with dismay as we came over the hill,
   Lookin' very warlike with our own pure whiskey still.
   We gave the enemy sweet poteen and the enemy gave three cheers;
   Who wants to fight and kill them lovely Dublin Fusiliers? (Chorus).

3. When we were broke our hearts were low, the Greeks we couldn't bate,
   But up came a decent officer with a great big canteen slate,
   We drank our belly fulls right up of the finest Dublin beer,
   And drowned the foe in vomit did the Dublin Fusiliers!   (Chorus).

4. Now when our history page is put in the glorious Golden Book
   Remember that there never was a bigger band of crooks,
   But when you're drinking pints of stout remember with a tear
   The men today who go without are the Dublin Fusiliers!   (Chorus).

27

EXILES

Words by Fintan Connolly. Music adapted from 'The Blackbird.

All— day in sor-row I — lie— sleep-less. To think — of to-mor-row makes me mourn-ful-ly sigh. Heart-sick — for your sake, the — task,— it seems hope-less. I do no-thing for my love but cry._____ Oh, — Rose a stoir, When will— you— e—ver the les-son— of — Life's— li—ving—learn? Put no faith in men who friend—ship— would— se—ver and from you for a for-tune turn. ___ The Sax— on—sword has en—ter'd deep-ly, O' Cav'-naugh is great no

more. _____ Dal - cas - sian and eu - gen - ian cold -

-heart-ed cow-ard - ly in - vite the hun- ter to our shores. _____

2.   The O'Mores and O'Connors, once in your vanguard,
Have turned to the Eastward and welcomed the foe
While you wait on alone for the sons of Fitzgerald
To come to arms and heal your woe.
When your sons lay dead at home all around you,
Dead with the proud sharp mark of the spear,
But now they set them free to go where none has found you,
To wander 'round the world in fear.

3.   He's free to sail away from your dear sorrow,
Free to unremember grief,
While the Saxon cold and proud waits on with time thus borrowed,
For waiting brings the foe relief.
Call, call them home, Love, home to stand around you.
Call them to stand like Milesians of old.
It's then a mighty guard will surround you
And take back the birthright sold!

*   A stor; - My Treasure.

Exiles 2

28

THE FAIR TORMENTOR

Translated from the Gaelic by Fintan Connolly. New Music.

One - eve-ning late I chanc'd to see her - by a

fun-'ral wake at - Mul-lagh-more My - love was trapp'd by this fair tor -

men-tor - such beau-ty, on - ly the god's a - dore. My

soul des-troy'd as I went up to her - no

sweet malt whis-ky can give me rest. My - heart once care-less till I did

view her - now seeks life's re - fuge in her fair breast.

2. To those hills behind me my thoughts keep going,
    And my sleep is broken by pained desire,
    To hold her slim waist, her lips bestowing
    Soft kisses over my heart on fire.
    My heart alone as the glens I wander;
    The sounds are false and the bird's note wrong,
    My shadow gone, and you to stand there
    Would be sweeter far then an Irish song.

3. My heart is heavy, it weighs inside me
    Like the dark clouds waiting before the rain,
    And the young cow leaping I stop to envy,
    For he plays beside her as I mourn again.
    In the wide lake near her I'd hold the waters
    And be satisfied as the gliding swan.
    I would'nt pine for fair Una's daughter
    Could I lie beside you, and me alone.

4. Oh, noble woman, are you me heeding?
    Is there anything you would have me do?
    No man of learning in the whole of Eireann
    Has words to say what I feel for you,
    For a miser's gold to ask is easy,
    And a royal princess I'd more quickly find;
    But it's you I want to lie beside me;
    Your love alone is my only mind.

The fair tormentor 2

29

FINEEN THE ROVER

Words and music remade by Dominic Behan

In an old cas-tle tow'r by the bil-lows - that

thun-der by Cleen-a's green strand, There dwelt as gal-lant a ro-ver - as

ev-er grasp'd hilt to the hand. Eight state-ly towr's o'er the wa-ters - lie

an-chor'd near Gal-ti-more Bay And ov-er there twen-ty score sail-ors -

who but the ro-ver holds sway. Then - Slain-te, Fin-een the

CHORUS

ro-ver - Fi-neen o' Dris-coll the free

tall as the mast of his gal-leys - and wild as the might of the sea.

2.   They boasted no tide could defy them,
     They ruled every wave on the main,
     But when they met Fineen the Rover
     Their proud star was soon on the wain.
     He gave them a breakfast of cutlass,
     Hot powder he sent them for tea,
     And for dinner, the best he could offer,
     He blew them right out of the sea!
     Chorus:

3.   The Saxons of Cork, aye, and Mallow,
     They harried his lands with their powers,
     But he gave them a taste of his cannon
     And drove them like wolves from his towers.
     The men of Clan London brought over
     A strong fleet to make him their slave,
     But he met them by Mizzen's green headland
     Where the sharks crunched their bones 'neath the waves!
     Chorus:

4.   Long years in that ould battered castle,
     Or out on the waves with his Clan
     He feasted and ventured and conquered
     And never struck colour to man.
     In a fight 'gainst the foes of his Country
     He died as a brave man should die,
     And he sleeps 'neath the waters of Cleena
     Where the waves sing his caoin* to the sky.
     Chorus:

     * Caoin : - mourning song. Pronounced - Cain.

Fineen the Rover 2

30 FINNEGAN'S WAKE

Arranged and adapted by Dominic Behan.

Tim Fin-ne-gan lived in Wat-ling Street a gent-le-man I - rish

ve - ry odd, He had a brogue most rich and sweet for to

rise in the world he car-ried a hod But Tim had a touch of the

tipp-ler's way with the love of the li-queur he was born

And to send him on his way each day he'd a drop of the cra - ter ev-'ry morn

Whack fo di do dance to your part-ner welt the floor with yer trot-ters shake,

Is-n't it the truth I'm tel-ling yeh? lots of fun at Fin-ne-gan's wake.

2. One morning Tim was rather full;
   His head felt heavy which made him shake.
   He fell from a ladder and broke his skull,
   So they took him home, his corpse to wake.
   They wrapped him up in a linen sheet
   And layed him out on top of the bed
   With a bucket of whiskey at his feet
   And a barrel of porter at his head.
   Chorus:

3. His friends assembled at the wake
   And then his widow called for lunch,
   First they brought in tea and cakes,
   Then pipes, tobacco, and brandy punch.
   Missus Biddy O'Brien began to cry
   "Such a lovely corpse did yeh ever see?"
   "Oh Tim a gradh, why did yeh die?"
   "Ah, hould yer gob!" said Molly McGee.
   Chorus:

4. Then Biddy O'Connor took up the job,
   "Oh Biddy", said she "yer wrong, I'm sure."
   But the other Biddy fetched her a belt on the gob
   And left her sprawling on the floor.
   Civil war did then engage
   Woman to woman, and man to man;
   Shilelagh law was all the rage,
   And a row and a ruction soon began.
   Chorus:

5. Jack Malony ducked his head
   When a bucket of whiskey flew at him;
   He ducked, and falling on the bed,
   The whiskey scattered over Tim!
   Bedad, he revives, and see how he rises,
   Finnegan rising in the bed saying
   "Whirl yer whiskey around like blazes.
   "Thunderin' jazez! did yis think me dead?"
   Chorus:

Finnegan's Wake 2

31
GET ME DOWN ME PETTICOAT

Words and Music by Dominic Behan

Oh - get me down me pet-ti - coat

get me down me shawl, Get me down me pet-ti-coat I'm

off to the *li-nen hall With a he was a *quare one

fol di do yeh gow a dat he was a quare one I'll tell you.

2.   Now, if he has joined the army all under a false name
        Just for to do me out of me pension, it's his oul *wan is to blame.
Chorus: He was a quare one....etc.

3.   She never really liked me, and I detested her.
        She thought her son too good for me - the dirty little cur!
        He was a quare one....etc.

4. She encouraged him to leave me to go away and fight,
    But she'll never rob me pension book, 'cos I'm his rightful wife!
    He was a quare one....etc.

5. If you go to the Curragh Camp ask for number nine,
    You'll find three squaddies standing there, and the best looking one is mine!
    He was a quare one....etc.

6. God help him, for a soldier's life he really was not meant;
    Would he be the tallest leprechaun or the smallest giant in the regiment?
    He was a quare one....etc.

7. But when he gets to the battle-line out there to fight the Boers,
    For God's sake hold the Dublins back, let the bogmen go before!
    He was a quare one....etc.

8. And when the war is over, when you're comin' back
    Make sure yeh bring a bit of plunder, wrap it up in your oul kit-sack!
    He was a quare one....etc.

    * 1.   Linen Hall - Where the British Army pensions were paid in Dublin.
    * 2.   A quare one....etc. - A queer one fol di do you get out of that'.
    * 3.   Aul wan   - Slang term for 'a mother'.

Get me down me petticoat 2

HOW CAESAR
WAS DRIVEN FROM IRELAND

Adapted and arranged by Dominic Behan from the original by John Crawford Wilson

2. Disguised in a pair of ould britches, Frieze coat, sturdy boots and caubeen*
   He scrambled through hedges and ditches to where the wake lights could be seen.
   Setting out very fearless and hearty he arrived somewhat soon in the night.
   Before me bould men at the party were quite drunk enough for a fight.

3. King Brian Boru* sat and eyed him, so also did huge Finn Macool*,
   While another man had there beside him a crozier propped up by a stool.
   To Caesar a pipe was extended by him with the crozier and cloak,
   But Caesar refused, quite offended said "Cities must blaze when I smoke!"

4. "Is that so", says another quite civil, "Yeh'll need a big pipe for that same".
   "If yeh think so ", says Caesar, quite livid, " I'm damned if yeh know then me name! "
   "Your name and your fame ", said the other, "Would both be much safer at home! "
   "The bogs of ould Ireland would smother a heathen come over from Rome! "

5. Then Caesar jumped up in a hurry and turned for to run to the door;
   All laughed, for he found in his flurry, his two feet were stuck to the floor.
   "What are yeh? Yer glances appal me", the other replied with a smile.
   "Saint Patrick me countrymen call me. I'm the guardian of Erin's green Isle".

6. Caesar stood, seeming wanting to linger, but Brian Boru bade him go.
   Saint Patrick he lifted his finger, and Finn Macool lifted his toe.
   He shot from the spot like a rocket, for Finn Macool kicked with a will.
   His men on the beach felt the shock, it electrified valley and hill!
   CODA:

* 1.   Brian Boru: - High king of Ireland in the early part of the 11th century.
* 2.   Finn Macool:- Legendary Irish giant. (Also Irish factual hero).
* 3.   Saint Patrick:- Patron Saint of Ireland.

How Caesar was driven from Ireland 2

33

IRISH ASTRONOMY

Arranged and adapted by Dominic Behan from the original by C.G.Halpine

O' Ry-an was a man of might when Ire-land was a na-tion. But poa-ching was his heart's de-light and con-stant oc-cu-pa-tion, He own'd an old mi-li-tia gun and cer-tain sure his aim was, He gave the keep-ers ma-ny a run for he did-n't care for game laws.

2.   Saint Patrick once was passin' by O'Ryan's little holdin'.
    And as the Saint was feelin' dry he though he'd have a stroll in,
    "'Ryan", said the Saint, "a mhic*, to preach at church I'm goin'
    "For God's sake let me have a rasher quick and a drop of Inishowen".

3.   Says Ryan, "No rasher's good for you while better I've to spare, sir,
    "But here's a jug of the mountain dew and there's a rattlin' hare sir".
    Saint Patrick he looked nighty sweet, says he, "Say God attend yeh,
    "And when yer in yer winding sheet it's up above I'll send yeh".

4.   Bould Ryan gave his pipe a whiff, "Them tidings is transportin'
    "But would yer saintship tell me if there's any kind of sporting?"
    Saint Patrick said, "A lion's there, two bears a bull and Cancer".
    "Begod", says Mick, "The huntin's rare. Saint Paddy, I'm yer man, Sir".

5.   So to conclude my song alright, for fear I'd tire your patience,
    You'll see O'Ryan any night amid them constellations.
    And Venus follows in his tracks while Mars grows jealous daily,
    But begod he fears the Irish knack of handling the shilelagh*.

*1.   A mhic : my son. Pronounced a vick.
*2.   Shilelagh : an Irish cudgeol. Pronounced shilalee.

JOE BRADY

Arranged and adapted' by Dominic Behan

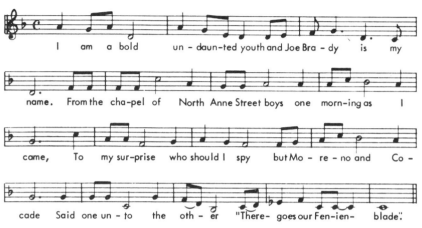

I am a bold un-daun-ted youth and Joe Bra-dy is my
name. From the cha-pel of North Anne Street boys one morn-ing as I
came, To my sur-prise who should I spy but Mo-re-no and Cocade Said one un-to the oth-er "There-goes our Fen-ien-blade".

2.   I didn't know the reason why they ordered me to stand,
I didn't know the reason why they gave me such a commend,
But when I saw James Carey* there I knew I was betrayed
But I'll face death before dishonour like a true born Fenian blade.

3.   They marched me up North Anne Street, boys, without the least delay,
The people standing on the path it filled them with dismay,
My sister cried, "I'll see yeh Joe, if ould Mallin* gives me leave,
"Keep up your heart for Ireland, boy, like a true born Fenian blade".

4.   It happened in the Phoenix Park all in the month of May,
Lords Cavendish and Burke* came out for to watch the polo play,
James Carey gave a signal, a handkerchief he waved,
But he gave full information about the Fenian blades.

5.   It was in Kilmainham Prison the Invincibles* were hung,
Mrs. Kelly* she was there in mourning for her son,
She threw back her shawl and said to all "Though he falls to a limepit grave,
"My son was no informer, boys, he died a Fenian Blade".

*1.   Moreno and Cocade : two policemen. *2. James Carey : a police informer.
*3.   Mallin : an Englishman in charge of security in Ireland. *4. The Invincibles : a
revolutionary group with Narodniki characteristics during the Parnellite era.
*5.   Cavendish and Burke : Vice Regent and Lord Lieutenant assassinated by the Invincibles
on their arrival in Ireland. The Vice-Regal lodge was situated in the Phoenix
Park, Dublin. *6. Mrs. Kelly : Mother of Tim Kelly one of the convicted men.

35 JOHNNY, I HARDLY KNEW YEH

Arranged and adapted by Dominic Behan

While go-ing the road to sweet A-thy ha - roo, - ha -
roo, - While go-ing the road to sweet A-thy ha - roo.___
While go-ing the road to sweet A - thay with
stick in her hand and a tear in her eye a dole - ful dam - sel
I did spy - Say-ing, "John-ny I hard-ly knew yeh!"

2. "Where is the leg with which yeh run haroo haroo?
"Where is the leg with which yeh run haroo?
"Where is the leg with which yeh run when first the enemy pointed a gun?
"I'm thinkin' yer dancing days are done, Johnny I hardly knew yeh.

3. "Where is the eye that looked so mild haroo haroo?
"Where is the eye that looked so mild haroo?
"Where is the eye that looked so mild when my poor heart yeh first beguiled?
"Why did yeh skidaddle from me and yer child? Johnny I hardly knew yeh.

4. "Yeh haven't an arm yeh haven't a leg haroo haroo,
"Yeh haven't an arm yeh haven't a leg haroo,
"Yeh haven't an arm yeh haven't a leg, yer an eyeless, noseless, chickenless egg,
"Yeh'll have to be put into a bowl to beg. Johnny I hardly knew yeh.

5. "With their drums and guns and drums and guns haroo haroo,
"With their drums and guns and drums and guns haroo.
"With their drums and guns and guns and drums the enemy nearly slew yeh,
"Oh darlin' dear yeh look so queer, Johnny I hardly knew yeh.

6. "But yeh'll never go to war again haroo haroo,
"Against much better fighting men haroo,
"For they showed yeh how to run me boy the whole way home to sweet Athy,
"Oh darlin'! Did yeh come home to die? Johnny I hardly knew yeh".

JOIN THE BRITISH ARMY 36

Adapted and arranged by Dominic Behan

When I was young I used to be as fine a man as you could see The Prince of Wales he said to me "Come join the Bri-tish ar-my." Too-ra-loo-ra loo ra loo They're look-ing for mon-keys in the zoo And if I had a face like you I'd join the Bri-tish ar-my.

2. Corporal Daly's gone away. His wife is in the family way;
   The only thing that she can say is "Blame the British Army!"
   Chorus:

3. Sergeant Doyle, he has the drought. Give him a load of Guiness' stout.
   He'll beat the enemy with his mouth to save the British Army!
   Chorus:

4. Kilted soldiers wear no drawers. Won't yeh kindly lend them your's?
   The poor should always help the poor. God help the British Army!
   Chorus:

5. They'll beat the Germans without fuss and lay their bones out in the dust;
   I know, for they quite near beat us – the gallant British Army!
   Chorus:

37 THE KERRY BOATMAN

Collected from Peter O'Toole arranged with new words by Dominic Behan

I wish I was - in Car - rick - fer - gus, in -
El - phin, Aoid-trim or Bal-ly - grind, Now I'd swim o - ver the deep-est
o - cean, the - deep-est o-cean my love to find. But the seas are -
deep, I can-not swim o - ver nei-ther have I el-wings____ to fly, I wish I
had - a hand-some boats-man to - fer - ry o - ver my love and I.

2. The night was dark and the storm uneasy, the mighty ocean gone black and wild,
When my own true love sweet Breedeen Vesey sailed far away and left me behind,
Left me behind to count my losses and see my dying in every glass,
Oh short is living and yet in cryin' how long the long night does take to pass.

3. And in Kilkenny it is reported on marble stones there as black as ink,
That with gold and silver I would support her, ah I'll sing no more till I've had a drink.
But I've been drinking I'm seldom sober, a constant rover from town to town,
Now I'm sick and me days are over, come Maur astore * and I'll lay me down.

*Astore: - My Treasure.

KIMMAGE

Children's street parody on Galway Bay. Adapted with new words by Dominic Behan

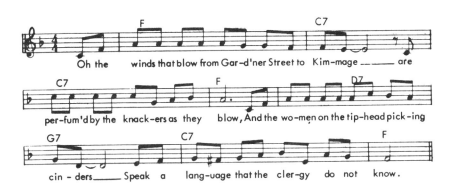

Oh the winds that blow from Gar-d'ner Street to Kim-mage _____ are per-fum'd by the knack-ers as they blow, And the wo-men on the tip-head pick-ing cin - ders_____ Speak a lang-uage that the cler-gy do not know.

2. If yeh ever have to go and live in Kimmage
    Make sure yeh have a blanket 'round her ma,
    For the climate in them houses in the country
    Is colder than in North Siberia!

3. There's a plot around the house that's called a garden,
    It's covered with black dirt that they call clay,
    And if yeh thinks it looks like muck yeh could be pardoned,
    It's the image of the stuff that's under hay!

4. If yer Mother pays the rent for two weeks runnin'
    The Polis will have questions without fail,
    And if she cannot tell them where she got the money
    They will drag your poor oul fella off to jail!

5. But someday I'll go back again to Kimmage,
    Be it only at the closing of my mind,
    To see again the children bate their grannies,
    Or tripping up the crippled and the blind!

39

THE LANDLORD AND
THE LEPRECHAUN

Words and music adapted by Wolfe Stephens.

To church on a Sun-day the land-lord re-tires to pray for ex-emp-tion from nick and his fires Well he asked an oul fai-ry to live in a shoe "Be-god said the elf "I don't mind if I do."

2. Well the toe of the shoe was a self contained deal
But the bathroom was shared by those renting the heel
Says the landlord, "the rent is as much as I screw".
Says the fairy, "I know you won't mind if yeh do".

3. Says the fairy "Begod upon me small soul.
"This house is too small for me large pot of gold".
Says his soul, "Put a spell on the landlordly crew".
"Begod", says the elf, "I don't mind if I do".

4. Well the landlords of London strange though it tell
Were all on the pan when me man cast his spell.
With their bottoms stuck tight, consternation it grew,
Says the fairy delighted, "Look what I can do".

5. "Release us", they cried in the voice of one man
"For it's not dignified to be stuck on the pan".
"I will", says the fairy, "release you from the lu,
"If to my questions you say I don't mind if I do".

6. Well the landlords all swore they'd do all sorts of things,
They'd reduce rents galore and let all live like kings.
"Now free us dear leprechaun, free us please do,
"For it's cold on the end when you sit in the lu".

7. Well the leprechaun merely ignored all their pleas,
"I'm off back to Ireland to live at my ease,
"If in elves you believe you're a stupid old crew,
"And not fit to live anywhere else but the lu".

THE LEE

40

Words and music by Dominic Behan

Could I see the green hills of my child - hood and the mist hang-ing low on the fields. Then this North-ern A - me - ri - can vil - lage, would - seem more like heav - en to me. But, - crowd-ing a - round in my dream - ing, are things I no long - er can see Like the pla-ces I've al -ways been leav - ing, since I wand-ered a - way from the Lee. Ev - 'ry

When the

2. Every man has a thought to go roaming,
    For far foreign fields are more green
    Than the fields of the land he was born in,
    The world that he never has seen.
    They told me when leaving my Ireland
    A new life would open for me,
    But now how I long for my Ireland
    And my old life at home by the Lee.

3. When the dust bowl has blown all around me
    And weary I dry from my eyes
    Not the sand which is seeking to hound me
    But the stars of my blue Irish skies.
    This Canadian land is a rare one,
    With work flowing plenty and free,
    But the vision I have is a fair one,
    At home by the banks of the Lee.

© Copyright 1964, CODA MUSIC LIMITED,

41

THE LEG

Words and music by Wolfe Stephens

2. A surgeon then spoke to this wealthy old yoke
    - A Harley Street man of the finest vocation -
    Who needed a limb for his colleagues and him
    To practise upon it anatomisation.
    He said that the leg had some rare gangrene
    The oddest uniquest he ever had seen,
    And after the rich merchant's feelings were preened
    The old eejit agreed to a rare amputation.

3. The oul doctor cried as he chopped down the side,
    "By my knife I ne'er lied, but one fork you are lacking,
    But you'll never need talk about crutches to stalk
    You'll have a fine leg of cork so I'd better get cracking"
    An artist it seemed who made cork legs his theme
    Which were driven by steam and as strong as a beam,
    Agreed to make one that would go like a gun
    And for walkin' or runnin' would never be slacking.

4. The leg fitted tight to the rich man's delight
    And with pride he invited the townsfolk to cop it.
    He walked round and round in and out of the town
    When the leg met high ground sure he told him to hop it.
    But the leg getting bored as the rich fellow roared
    Away then it soared with its owner aboard
    At first a slow pace then a nice steady chase
    When it started to race sure nobody could stop it.

5. Well, the rich fella's plight as he held on so tight
    In a terrible fright was right wondrous funny,
    Over valleys and bogs never ceasing to jog
    Till soon he was lost to the town of kilcroney.
    Over oceans he soared as he roared and implored
    But the leg ne'er accorded a heed to his words.
    And I'll bid you goodnight as he goes out of sight
    And the poor man as right makes away with his money.

The Leg 2

42

THE LIMERICK RAKE

Collected from Stephen Behan of Dublin.
Tune adapted by Dominic Behan.

I am a young fel-la that's eas-y and bold, In Cas-tle-town Con-nor I'm ve-ry well known. In New-cas-tle West I've spent ma-ny a note with Kit-ty and Ju-dy and Ma-ry. Me Fa-ther re-prov'd me for be-ing such a rake, and for spend-ing me time in such fro-lic-some ways, But I could not for-get the good na-ture of Jane; *A-gas fa-ga-maid siud mar a-ta se.

2.   Me parents they taught me to reap and to sow
      To plough and to harrow to plant and to mow,
      But me mind being too grand for to drop it so low
      I embarked on a high speculation.
      On paper and parchment they taught me to write,
      And in Latin and Euclid they opened my eyes,
      And in multiplication of course I was bright;
    * Agas fagamaid siud mar ata se.

3.   To quarrel for riches I'm never inclined,
      For the greatest of misers must leave them behind.
      I'll buy me a cow that can never run dry,
      And to milk her I'll twist the left horn.
      John Damer of Shronel has plenty of gold,
      And there's more with the misers of Galway, I'm told,
      But old John's on his back among nettles and stones;
      Agas fagamaid siud mar ata se.

4.   There's some say I'm foolish, there's none says I'm wise.
      Being fond of the women is not such a crime,
      For the Son of King David had ten hundred wives,
      And such wisdom 't'was even recorded.
      I'll dig a good garden and live at me ease,
      And each woman of mine can partake of the same,
      If they war with each other themselves have the blame;
      Agas fagamaid siud mar ata se.

5.   But now, for the future, I think I'll act wise,
      And send for the women that held me so kind.
      I'll marry them all when I manage the time
      If the clergy agree to the bargain.
      And when I'm down below and me soul is at peace
      Those women will come and all cry at me wake,
      And me sons and their daughters will offer their prayers
      To the Lord for the soul of their father!

*   Agas fagamaid siud mar ata se: - Pronounced 'Awgus fawgumeed
                                    shewed mawr a taw shay'.
      Meaning: - We'll leave it as it is.

The Limerick Rake 2

43

LILLI BULERO

Arranged and adapted from the original of Thomas Lord Wharton by Dominic Behan.

Ho bro-ther Taigh doth hear the de-cree Lil-li Bu-le - ro bul-len-a - la

Ire-land's to have a new de-pu-ty Lil-li Bu-le - ro bu -len-a - la.

CHORUS

Le - ro Le - ro Lil-li-Bu-le - ro Lil-li-Bu - le - ro bul-len-a -la

Le - ro le - ro Lil-li-Bu-le - ro Lil-li-Bu - le - ro bul-len-a - la.

2. Well be me soul, it is a Talbot!
Lilli bulero bullen a la,
And he will cut all the Englishmens' throats.
Lilli bulero bullen a la.
Chorus:

3. And if dispensation comes from the Pope
Lilli bulero bullen a la.
We'll hang Magna Carta and them from a rope.
Lilli bulero bullen a la.
Chorus:

4. Hear how in France they all prattle and swear
Lilli bulero bullen a la.
That there will be a Protestant heir.
Lilli bulero bullen a la.
Chorus:

5. Ah, but if that be so, why stays he behind?
   Lilli bulero bullen a la.
   Take it from me, it's a Protestant wind.
   Lilli bulero bullen a la.
   Chorus:

6. But can it be true, is Tyrconnel ashore?
   Lilli bulero bullen a la.
   It **is**! And he hands out commissions galore.
   Lilli bulero bullen a la.
   Chorus:

7. Then who will not go on to the Mass?
   Lilli bulero bullen a la.
   Shall be turned out to look like an ass?
   Lilli bulero bullen a la.
   Chorus:

8. Then the heretics all will go down,
   Lilli bulero bullen a la.
   By Christ and Saint Patrick
                    the Nation's our own.
   Lilli bulero bullen a la.
   Chorus:

9. There was an ould prophecy found in a bog
   Lilli bulero bullen a la.
   That Ireland be ruled by an ass and a dog.
   Lilli bulero bullen a la.
   Chorus:

10. And now that the prophecy has come to pass
    Lilli bulero bullen a la,
    King James is the Dog, King Billy's the Ass.
    Lilli bulero bullen a la!
    Chorus:

Lillie Bulero 2

44 LIVERPOOL LOU

Words and music by Dominic Behan.

Oh Li-ver-pool Lou, love-ly Li-ver-pool Lou_____ why

don't you be - have, just like oth-er - girls do_____

Why must my poor heart keep fol-low - ing you_____

stay home and love me, my Li - ver - pool Lou._____ When

I go a - walk - ing_____ hear peo-ple talk - ing___
sounds from the ri- ver_____keep tell-ing me ev - er___

_____ school chil-dren play - ing,_____ I know what they're say -
_____ that I should for - get you_____ Like I'd nev - er met

ing____ They're say-ing - you'll grieve me ____ that
you____ tell me their song love ____ was

you will de- ceive me ____ Some morn-ing you'll leave
nev-er more wrong love____ say I be - long

me____ all packed up and gone. Oh! Liv-er-pool Lou,
love____ to my Liv-er - pool Lou.

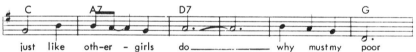

love - ly Liv-er-pool Lou____ why don't you be -have,

just like oth-er - girls do_____ why must my poor

heart keep fol-low - ing you____ stay home and love

me, my Li - ver - pool Lou.____ The -

Liverpool Lou 2

45

LOVE IS TEASING

Words and music remade by Dominic Behan

wish - I was in - love a-gain But I know that my wish-ing is all in vain. For al-ways and ev - er my fam - i - ly make fun of the love that you have - for me. They

CHORUS

say love is teas-ing, - love is pleas-ing love is a treas-ure,when first it's new, but as it grows old - er - love grows col-der,'til it fades-a-way like the morn-ing dew.

2. I'd leave my Father, I'd leave my Mother, I'd leave my sisters and brothers too,
   But I know when I'm gone I'll still hear their song, of how
   Love fades away like the morning dew.
   Chorus:

3. I'll take a notion to cross the ocean, and leave my family and friends behind,
   Where I'll never be near them, no more to hear them
   Singing those words that disturb my mind.
   Chorus:

LOVE OF MY HEART

46

Translated with new music by Wolfe Stephens.

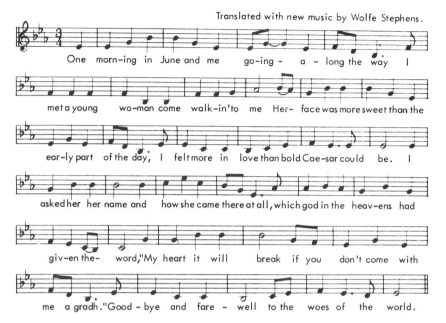

One morn-ing in June and me go-ing - a - long the way I met a young wo-man come walk-in'to me Her- face was more sweet than the ear-ly part of the day, I felt more in love than bold Cae-sar could be. I asked her her name and how she came there at all, which god in the heav-ens had giv-en the- word,"My heart it will break if you don't come with me a gradh."Good - bye and fare - well to the woes of the world.

2. "Well, I'm a young girl from close by the water's edge,
"And reared very pure since the day I was born,
"I being very airy I from my own people fled,
"For me and my parents could not get along."
"Oh treasure, " says I, "Come listen to me a spell,
"I'll give you a story that's straight from my heart,
"If yeh don't come with me I'd much rather go live in Hell, "
Goodbye and farewell to the woes of the earth.

3. "Go on now yeh rogue, you're anxious to get to bed,
"But I know an ould man with a bit of a farm,
"And a bird in the hand is worth two when they're overhead
"And the thought of his money will keep me quite warm."
"Oh, I have no oats, barley wheat, or that kind of thing,
"But a blanket tonight all round us shall be furled
"And I'll buy you a dress and a sort of marriage ring."
Goodbye and farewell to the woes of the earth.

4. "There's an alehouse nearby and we will lie till morning there,
"If that satisfies you my sweet treasure store,
"And we'll send for the priest for to make you and I a pair,
"In front of the world and they won't know the score.
"As long as the money lasts we two will drinking be
"Then homeward we'll go on the wings of a bird,
"When the reckoning is paid who cares for the landlady?"
Goodbye and farewell to the woes of the world.

© Copyright 1965. CODA MUSIC LIMITED,

47

LONELY DAYS

New words, and tune adpated by Dominic Behan.

2.   It wasn't me that spoke them words, they were not spoke by me
Those words were said by him now dead, his name is jealousy my love
His name is jealousy.

3.   I met a girl you call your friend I listened as she spoke
When I left her then to call on you, my heart it nearly broke my love
My heart it nearly broke.

4.   With anger in my heart my love, I saw you smile at me
But I thought your smile was for other men, my thoughts was jealousy my love,
My thoughts was jealousy.

5.   Put away those words, come walk with me
Come stop your rambling ways
Forgive my thoughts my jealousy,
That made them lonely days my love
That made them lonely days.

MAIDS
WHEN YOU'RE YOUNG

Words and music adapted by Dominic Behan

An old man came court-ing me ri - ti and too - ra - li An old man came court-in' me, me be-ing young, An old man came court-in' me ri - ti and too - ra - li Maids when you're young ne-ver wed an ould man.

2. When we stood at the rails riti and toorali,
    When we stood at the rails, and me being young,
    When we stood at the rails I thought me heart would fail.
    Maids, when yer young never wed an ould man.

3. When we went to our beds riti toorali,
    When we went to our beds, me being young,
    When we went to our beds he went to sleep instead.
    Maids, when yer young never wed an ould man.

4. He had no riti fol do and doorali.
    He had no riti, me being young.
    He had no riti, no time for fol doorali.
    Maids, when yer young never wed an ould man.

5. When he lay fast asleep riti toorali,
    When he lay fast asleep, me being young,
    When he lay fast asleep what did I do but creep
    Into the arms of a lovely young man!

6. He had the wish to play riti toorali,
    He had the wish to play, me being young,
    He had the wish to play all night till break of day.
    Maids, when yer young always wed a young man!

49

MASTER McGRATH

Arranged and adapted by Dominic Behan

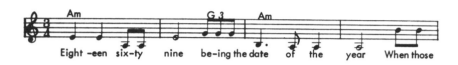

Eight-een six-ty nine be-ing the date of the year When those

Wa-ter-loo sports-men and more did ap-pear To

gain the great priz-es and to bear it a-wa' Nev-er

count-in' on Ire-land and Mas-ter Mc-Grath.

2. On the twelfth of December, that day of renown,
    McGrath and his keeper they left Lurgan Town;
    A gale in the Channel it soon drove them o'er.
    On the thirteenth they landed on fair England's shore.

3. And when they arrived there in big London Town
    Those great English sportsmen all gathered around,
    And some of them laughed with a scornful "Ha Ha",
    Saying "Is that the great dog you call Master McGrath?"

4. And one of those gents, from his nose looking down,
    Said "I don't care a damn for your Irish greyhound!"
    And another he sneers with a scornful "Ha Ha"
    "We'll soon humble the pride of your Master McGrath!"

5.   Lord Lurgan stepped forward and said "Gentlemen,
        "If there's any among you has money to spend,
        "For you nobles of England we don't care a straw,
        "Here's five thousand to one upon Master McGrath."

6.   McGrath he looked up and he wagged his ould tail
        Informing his Lordship "I can see what yeh mean.
        "Don't mind them, dear Lurgan. Don't heed them a gradh.
        "I'll soon cripple their laughter", said Master McGrath.

7.   There stood Rose Of England, the Saxon's great pride;
        The Master, quite easy, was close by her side;
        They let her away and the crowd cried "Hurrah!
        "For the pride of all England – and Master McGrath!"

8.   As Rose and the Master they both ran along,
        "I wonder", asked Rose, "what took you from your home?
        "You should have stayed there in your Irish demesne,
        "And not tried to gain laurels on Albion's plains!"

9.   "Now I know", said McGrath, "we have wild heather bogs,
        "But you'll find in old Ireland there's good men and dogs:
        "Lead on, bould Brittania, give none of yer jaw.
        "Shove that up yer nostrils!" says Master McGrath.

10.   The hare ran on with a wonderful view,
        And swift as a rocket it crossed Waterloo;
        Rose gave the first turn, which is according to law,
        For the second was given by Master McGrath.

11.   McGrath paced the hare just as swift as the wind.
        He was sometimes before it, and sometimes behind.
        Then he jumped on her back and he held up his paw;
        "We've beaten the Saxons!" said Master McGrath.

Master McGrath 2

50 THE MAN FROM WEXFORD

Arranged and adapted by Dominic Behan

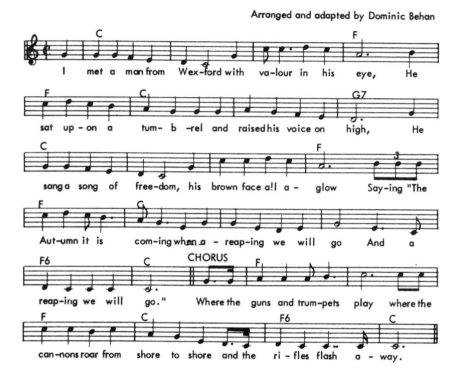

I met a man from Wex-ford with va-lour in his eye, He
sat up-on a tum-b-rel and raised his voice on high, He
sang a song of free-dom, his brown face all a - glow Say-ing "The
Aut-umn it is com-ing when a - reap-ing we will go And a
reap-ing we will go." Where the guns and trum-pets play where the
can-nons roar from shore to shore and the ri-fles flash a - way.

CHORUS

2.   "And what will be our harvest" he answered them with scorn,
     "I'll tell you what we'll gather in on our first reaping morn',
     The scarlet Saxon soldiers all standing in a row,
     We'll cut them down like corn when a-reaping we will go
     And a-reaping we will go..."
     Chorus:

3.   "And where shall we bring the harvest where shall we bring the corn,
     Where shall be our harvest home on our last reaping morn'
     Dublin's royal Castle will make a gallant show
     With the green flag flyin' o'er it when a-reaping we will go
     And a-reaping we will go...
     Chorus:

4.   And who will smile upon us and bless our flashing arms,
     Who will be our Queen of Hope in battles loud alarms?
     Our own beloved Ireland, no other Queen we'll know,
     We'll die for her or conquer when a-reaping we will go
     And a-reaping we will go..."
     Chorus:

THE MERRY PLOUGHBOY 51

Words and music adapted by Dominic Behan

I am a mer-ry plough-boy and I plough'd the fields by day Un-til the light-'ning flashed a - cross my mind that I should run a-way, I've al-ways hat-ed sla-ver - y since the day that I was born, So I'm off to join the I. R. A. And I'm off to-mor-row morn'.

CHORUS:

I'm off to Dub-lin in the green, in the green, Where bay-on-ets—— glist-ened in the sun; Where the rif -les flashed, and the thun-der crashed to the ec- ho of a Thomp-son gun. ——

2. I leave aside my old gray coat, I leave aside my plough,
I leave aside my horse and yoke for no more I'll need them now,
I'll take my short revolver and my bandolier of lead,
And live or die I can but try to avenge my country's dead.
Chorus:

3. There's one I leave behind me, the cailin* I adore
I wonder will she think of me when she hears them cannons roar.
But when the war is over and dear old Ireland's free,
I'll take her to the church to wed and a rebel's wife she'll be.
Chorus:

* Cailin : - Girl.

52

(MIGHTY MILLHOUSE)
ARKLE

Words and music by Dominic Behan

It hap-pened in the spring-time of the year of six - ty four, When

Eng-lish-men were mak-ing pounds and fiv - ers by the score He

beat them in the hol-lows and he beat them on the bumps A

pair of fan - cy fet-locks he showed them o'er the jumps.

2.   He's English! He's English! As English as you've seen
    A little bit of Arab stock and more from Stephen's Green
    Take a look at Mill House and throw out your chest with pride
    He's the greatest steeplechaser an the English countryside.

3.   Then a quiet man called Dreaper livin' in the Emerald Isle
    Said"That horse of yours called Mill House surely shows a bit of style,
    "But I've a little fella and Arkle is his name,
    "Put your money where you put your mouth and then we'll play the game."

4. Well the English racing gentleman laughed till fit to burst,
    "You tried before Tom Dreaper and then you came off worst,
    "If you think your horse could beat us you're runnin' short on brains
    "It's Mill House that you want to fight and not those beastly Danes."

5. "Arkle now is five to two Mill House is money on,
    "They're off! and dear believe I do the Champion has it won,
    "There are other horses in the race to test the great chap's might
    "But deary me it's plain to see the rest are out of sight."

6. "There are three more fences now to go he leads by twenty lengths
    "Brave Arkle's putting in a show, poor chap he's all but spent,
    "Mill House sweeps on majestically great glory in each stride
    "He's the greatest horse undoubledly within the whole world wide.

7. "Two to go still Arkle comes he's cutting down the lead,
    "But he's beaten bar the shouting for he hasn't got th espeed,
    "They're on the run up to the last my God can he hold out,
    "Look behind you Willie Robinson man what are you about?

8. "They're at the last and over Pat Taffe has more in hand
    "He's passing England's Mill House the finest in the land,
    "My God he has us beaten! What can we English say?
    "The ground was wrong? The distance long? Too early early in the day?"

Arkle 2

53 MO BUACAILLAIN DONN

Arranged and adapted by Dominic Behan

My___ true love he dwells - on a moun - tain___ Like a war-eag-le fear-less and free, ___ By the side of a low - tun-ing foun-tain___ That - swings down thru' wild an-na - lee.___ His soul has more beau-ty and hon-our___ than - a king with a - pa-lace and crown ___ For the blood of the race of O' Con-nor ___ fills the veins of mo buac - ail -lain donn. ___

2. A soft Cead Mile Failte* I'll give him as he comes in the evening to me,
   And what would I do but believe him when he whispers a cushla mo croide*
   For his look is so truthful and tender from his soft rolling eyes of dark brown,
   That even a lady of splendour would be coaxed by mo buacaillain donn.

3. My Father has riches in plenty and suitors for me in his eye,
   But oh! let my age come to twenty till I bid them all the go by,
   For I long for a home in the mountains far away from the dust of the town,
   By the side of a low-tuning fountain and the love of mo buacaillain donn.

*1. Buacaillain Don : My Brown (Haired) boy. Pronounced vuucaleen down.
*2. Cead Mile Failte : One hundred thousand welcomes. Pronounced Kade meela faulte.
*3. Cushla mo croide : Joy of my heart. Pronounced cushla muh cree.

Mo Buacaillain Donn 2

54

THE MOUNTJOY HOTEL

New words, tune adapted by Dominic Behan

In Dub - lin's big town there are first - class ho -
tels Where they give board and lodg-ings to all the big swells They've
blinds on the win-dows and bells on the doors And beau-ti - ful
car-pets laid down on the floor It's in such a spot that you
get a great view of the Roy-al Can-al and the ships that pass
thru' I was there once my-self so I'm ab-le to
tell That there's no digs in Dub-lin like the Mount-joy Ho - tel.

2.   One stipulation of this fine resort–
        All lodgers must first be presented at Court
        And there recommended as suited and right
        To sleep in this mansion by day and by night:
        For there, I can say, are the cream of our land,
        Doctors and lawyers and men of that band.
        In the next suite to me, I remember full well,
        A duke spent nine months in the Mountjoy Hotel.

3.   For the entrance they've built up three beautiful gates,
        And once past the third one there's no need to wait;
        The butler just waves and he calls for the boots,
        "Fill a bath for this guest, and prepare him a suite."
        Without bye or lave ye he makes you at home,
        And sends for a barber to trim up your dome,
        And then, when he's finished, the clerk rings a bell;
        The manager meets all at the Mountjoy Hotel.

4.   One thing about this, all the service is free,
        Be ye higher or lower or middle degree.
        When ye feel like a change never reck the amount,
        You'll never be given a bill or account.
        I stopped there myself for close on five years,
        And when I was leaving the staff were in tears.
        "I wish you were spending" the manager said
        "The rest of your life at the Mountjoy Hotel."

The Mountjoy Hotel 2

55

MR. MURPHY'S
TAR-MACADAM HIGHWAYS

Words by, and music adapted by Wolfe Stephens

2. The Irish, Welsh and Scotsmen and the men from Africa
    Cannot complain, come wind or rain, we have the best, by far.
    They let us punch the tickets and clean out the gents' abodes,
    But better yet, they let us sweat for Murphy on the roads.
    (Chorus:)

3. It's early in the morning, for we rise at five o'clock;
    The poor old English have to stay still rolling in the flock,
    But we have the freedom of the town, such liberty untold,
    For our boss is Mister Murphy and his million London roads.
    (Chorus:)

4. For serving overseas a medal we have proudly won.
    'Twas in the dark days of the nights we built the great M.1.
    But the finest honour we did get, the story I will tell:
    We built the greatest highway through the fiery depths of Hell.
    (Chorus:)

5. Oul Satan says to Murphy "Get that shovel in your hand."
    Oul Murphy takes that shovel and he offers it to Dan.
    Black Dan, says he "We're equal here in this big black abode.
    There's no-one but yourself to dig your dirty bloody roads!"
    (Chorus:)

Mr. Murphy's Tar-Macadam Highways 2

MOTHER ENGLAND

Words by, and music adapted by Dominic Behan

Oh how gen - tle moth - er Eng - land when you're get - ting grey and old, You'll give free - dom to your co - lo - nies - the ones you can - not hold You'll - pose be - nign and lov - ing as de - fend - er of the weak, But there's one com - plaint you'll dodge and feint and ne - ver of it speak.

CHORUS

Oh you've pains a - round your Ken - ya, your Gui - a - na's not so hot Your Ma - lay - sia's turn - ing cy - pric your Rhodes di - sease has gone to pot. But you could eas - 'ly ov - er - come them with - out cal - cutting off your kong If your du - o - den - ial Ul - ster was - n't quite so wrong.

2. Wasn't it lovely when Victoria could go riding o'er the Rand
   Knowing well that loyal Pretoria was in the best of hands?
   She had Disraeli in her pocket, and Prince Albert by the head,
   And a fine big strapping Scotsman underneath the bed.
   Chorus:

3. Oh, when King Georgie ruled the waves - our well-loved sailor King,
   To think he'd let us be his slaves was enough to make us sing;
   And when those I. R. A. guerillas tried to push him from the land
   Was he angry? No! sound fellow, he sent over the Black and Tans.
   Chorus:

4. Oh Princess, we apologise, it's not like us at all
   To wait till darkness fills the skies and blow out your bedroom wall;
   But when the young have ancient memories, or they wouldn't misbehave,
   They say it's to do with a hanging or two and a million famine graves!
   Chorus:

Mother England 2

57

MRS. HOOLIGAN'S CHRISTMAS CAKE

New words and music adapted by Dominic Behan

As I sat in me wind-ow one eve-ning,_____ A let-ter man came un-to me,_____ With a nice lit-tle neat in-vit-ta-tion_____ Say-ing, "Won't yeh come ov-er to tea?"_____ I knew it was Hoo-li-gan sent it,_____ I went for old friend-ship sake,_____ But the first thing they gave me to tack-le_____ was a slice of Mis-sus Hoo-li-gan's cake._____

2. There were plums and prunes and berries, raisins and currants and cinnamon too,
   There were nuts and cloves and cherries, but the crust it was nailed on with glue.
   There were carraway seeds in abundance 'twould give you a fine headache.
   'Twould kill any man twice to be eating a slice of Mrs.Hooligan's Christmas cake.
   Chorus:

3. Mulligan wanted to taste it but really it wasn't no use.
   She worked at it over an hour but couldn't get any of it loose,
   Kelly came in with the hatchet and Hooligan sent for the saw,
   But all they succeeded in smashing was the hatchet and Kelly's left jaw.
   Chorus:

4. Then a little man worked in the army a soldier or some such like,
   He brought in a big box of matches and a hundredweight of gelignite,
   They went five hundred yards maybe seven and watched as the fuse flame raced
   The house rose upward to heaven but the confection was still in place.
   Chorus:

Mrs. Hooligan's Christmas Cake 2

58

MRS. McHUGH
HAS UP AND DIED

Children's street song, new words and music by Dominic Behan

Mis - sus Mc-Hugh has up and died up and died up and died

Mis - sus Mc-Hugh has up and died and by the priest an - noin - ted.

2. Who will be in charge of the wake in charge of the wake in charge of the wake?
   Who will be in charge of the wake, and Hoya is appointed.

3. See the mourners kneelin' down kneelin' down kneelin' down,
   See the mourners kneelin' down, their prayers grow ever shorter.

4. Because their prayers are unawares unawares unawares
   Because their prayers are unawares that they came here for a porter.

5. Now they're singin' short and low short and low short and low
   Now they're singin' short and low respect cos they're all sober.

6. But listen how the noise it grows the noise it grows the noise it grows,
   Listen how the noise it grows because they're half seas over.

7. Mrs. McHugh has up and died has up and died has up and died.
   Mrs. McHugh has up and died they've sent her soul to heaven

8. Mrs. McHugh has up and died has up and died has up and died
   Mrs. McHugh has up and died her next stop's Glas-a-nev-i-in*.

   * Glas-a-nev-i-in: - Dublin cemetery.

THE MURDERER'S DOG 59

New words and new music by Wolfe Stephens

Come all you cle-ver po-lis-men and lis-ten for a while I'll tell to you a thing or two that hap-pen'd in E-rin's Isle. You boast a-bout the way you go of sol-vin' ev-'ry crime But there was one right case where you got-the chase and on-ly just in time.

2. I'm talkin' of the murderer who freedom did enjoy
For many months when he had killed two citizens of Athboy,
He might have murdered half the town for all it meant to you
Had you not near tripped over a very important clue.

3. With courage fierce his knife did pierce his victims' gory breasts
And what's the use in talkin' loose cos people know the rest,
His victims cried, "By God I've died, from stab wounds to the heart,
Lift up me head for I'm half dead and now I must depart."

4. The murderin' man his filthy plan had almost right conceived,
And nothin' but the Will of God stopped his will to succeed,
Clear as the day he got away but then the Hand of God
Felt so inclined as to leave behind a witness in a dog.

5. However you seek no dog to speak will yeh ever come across,
But them beasts have powers that's not like ours for we'd be at a loss
To follow you and pick up a clue and a trail from a bit of a scent,
By the Holy Mose 'twas with his nose the dog made his statement.

6. All for that horrid murder convenient to Athboy
That left without his par-i-ents a decent Irish boy,
Fallin' on his bended knees for mercy the murderer cried,
The judge he said "No mercy, tomorrow you must die."

60
MY BONNY BROWN BOY

Arranged and adapted from the singing of Kathleen Behan by Dominic Behan

"Where have you been to my bon-ny brown boy?

Where have you been to my heart's love and joy?" "To the

fair in Bal-lin-tub-ber, moth-er make my bed soon For I'm

tired to the heart and I want to lie down.

2. "And what is your ailing my bonny brown boy?
    "What is your ailing, my heart's love and joy?"
    "My ailing is dying Mother make my bed soon,
    "For I'm tired to the heart and I want to lie down."

3. "What makes for your dying my bonny brown boy?
    "What makes for your dying my heart's love and joy?
    "A coach and six horses Mother make my bed soon
    "For I'm tired to the heart and I want to lie down."

4. "And what for your Father, my bonny brown boy?
    "What for your Father, my heart's love and joy?
    "I'm poisoned by my true love. Mother make my bed soon,
    "For I'm tiredto the heart, and I want to lie down."

5. "And what for your true love my bonny brown boy?
    "What for your true love, my heart's love and joy?"
    "My true love has left me Mother make my bed soon,
    "For I'm tired to the heart and I want to lie down."

6. "And what for your Mother, my heart's love and joy?"
    "What for your Mother, my heart's love and joy?"
    "The gates of Heaven I'll open, Mother make my bed soon
    "For I'm tired to the heart and I want to lie down."

7. "And where shall we bury you my bonny brown boy?
    "Where shall we bury you my bonny brown boy?"
    "Put a stone at my haed and a stone at my feet,
    "And place me in Glasnevin for I but long to sleep."

THE NEW FREE STATERS

Words by Fintan Connolly, music remade

Sweet Ker - ry fair was far from where they mur-der'd brave O' Neill, There - were no kha - ki un - i - forms be - hind the flash-ing steel, The fir - ing squad, I swear by God, was not from Lond -on town, But I - rish boys, cute Eng - land's toys, cut Ire - land's he - ro down.

2.
On Tommy Harte and Pat McGrath, those young men did the same,
Dick Goss and Charlie Kerins too were butchered in the game,
Of English guns by Ireland's sons like Christ by Judas sold,
And none could say, 'twas for the pay, for England paid no gold.

3.
Look homeward, Eamonn of Bruree, 'tis time you dried your hands,
Wet with blood of liberty, the guts of Ireland,
We'll build a headstone to your grave to hold your memory,
Each yard of power a bloodstained hour, and Ireland still unfree!

62 NO LOVE NO MORE

Words and music by Dominic Behan

Oh the world's not - big e - nough no more _____ since that wo - man _____ walked right thru' that door _____ She walked right - out on me, she won't be sit-tin' boubt-in' me no more. Ain't about no more. To shout no more _____ All those mill-ions - of miles and not a place a man could hide, for-ev - er more _____ Ev - 'ry - for ev - er more _____ How can I for - get my wo - man when the world's full of love for - ev - er more _____

2. Everytime I sit down beneath a tree
    All the shadows they keep remindin' me
    Every sound from around me is her voice come to hound me
    Evermore.
    No good no more, no love no more.
    All those millions of acres not a place to escape her
    Anymore.

3. Every juke box shouts its loving song
    Of the lovers who so lovingly belong.
    When I see couples kissing it shows what I'm missing
    Makes me sore.
    Ain't fair no more, ain't fair no more.
    How can I forget that woman when the world's full of loving,
    Shore to shore - forever more.
    REFRAIN: as above.

63

NOT A STAR
FROM THE FLAG SHALL FADE

Music by Dominic Behan, Words adapted by Dominic Behan from the original
by C.G. Halpine

On a rare old - flag was the flag we bore a - brave - old - flag and
nice, It had stripes in plent - y and stars ga - lore, - the -
pro - duct of free - dom's de - vice We - car - ried it South we
car - ried it far - and a - round it our bi - vou - acs - made, _____ And we
swore by God that nev - er - a star from its a - zure field should fade.

2. The fight grows thick our brave boys fall, and the bullets like a banshee* scream,
And the flag though torn by many a ball, flies high over Liverty's dream,
Though pierced by shrapnel still it bears all the stars in its tattered field,
And again the brigade like one man swears not a star from the flag we yield.

3. The fight was won after many a year but a lot of the boys who bore
That flag from their wives and sweethearts dear returned to their homes no more.
They died by the bullet's awful power and to graves they were rudely tossed,
But the thought came warm in their dying hour, "Not a star from the flag was lost"

4. At Gettysburg when Lincoln spoke our gallant sixty-ninth
Knew well how fearful slavery's yoke proud freemen could anoint,
Our Irish hands round negro bands a common friendship made,
Our promise kept to our Motherland not a star in the flag did fade.

*Banshee : Bean Sigte, the Fairy Woman.

64

OH, GENTLE YOUTH

Translated, with new music by Fintan Connolly

Oh young man come tell me in whose bed last night you lay, Did you lie there - be - side me and no heed of hear-ing to me pay? If my sor-row was in your mind not one hour in sleep - would you bide: It was your grave clothes and they going by me left the sharp pain in my side.

2.	My praying is not answered and I shall kneel in prayer no more,
	My grey hair is withering - and I only lie to bed and moan;
	My hair grey and withering and falling softly like the mist.
	In blind sorrow for you my darling I no longer can exist.

3.	For the land of Clan Seoigeac* in the morn I'll hoist my sail,
	To see there my thousand treasures and look no more on where I came.
	Let them talk for I cannot hear since my loved one speaks to me no more,
	Not all Ireland could separate us if I was yours my treasure store.

4.	In the Autumn or Springtime I would need a useful man,
	For the barley must be in sheaves e'er the short days should lose their span,
	But a young boy I'd have beside me for I would live in mortal dread
	To share my love for gold and silver with a widower in bed.

*The Land of Clan Seoigeac: "The Joyce Country". Pronounced Shawack.

© Copyright 1965, CODA MUSIC LIMITED.

Written by John Macdonnell and translated by W.B.Guiney.
This version arranged adapted and set to music by Dominic Behan.

2. Can it be she whose history is in the mist of years?
   Whose kings of old wore crowns of gold and led ten thousand spears?
   Oh God! the change so sad and strange – her kings have passed away,
   New sons disdain to break thy chains sweet Erin in the sea.

3. Where are the men by tower and glen who held you safe before?
   And often gave your foes a grave on your exalted shore?
   Galglach and Kerne full sure and stern they fought to keep you free,
   Ah but they sleep and you must weep Old Erin in the sea.

4. And in their place a wretched race upon your soil has grown,
   With branded name, unfearing shame, forget their sires alone,
   They shun the claim of patriot fame and bend the servile knee,
   To kiss the yoke their Fathers broke in Erin of the sea.

5. You bards of song you warriors strong of high heroic deeds,
   All dust you be by mount and lea, while she your Mother bleeds,
   And cold the blood by fort and flood that ran her veins as free,
   As she was then when you had men Old Erin of the sea.

66

OUL LEATHER BRITCHES

Arranged and adapted from the singing of Stephen Behan by Dominic Behan

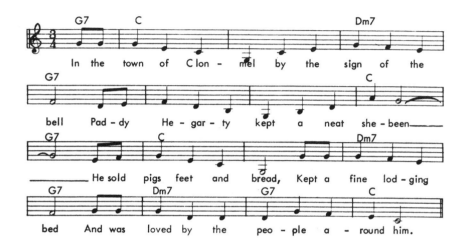

In the town of C lon - mel by the sign of the
bell Pad - dy He - gar - ty kept a neat she - been
He sold pigs feet and bread, Kept a fine lod - ging
bed And was loved by the peo - ple a - round him.

2.   For twenty-one years, at least so it appears,
Them britches his Father had run in,
And before the man died he to his bedside
Called Paddy, the eldest son to him.

3.   His advice then he gave e'er he went to the grave,
He bade him "Take care of me riches."
Says he "It's no use leapin' into me shoes,
But I'd like you to step into me britches."

4.   Well last Winter's snow, it left food very low,
Poor Paddy was ate out completely.
With the snow coming down he could not get to town;
Thoughts of hunger did trouble him greatly.

5.   One evening he lay dreaming away
Of ghosts, fairies, spirits and witches,
When he heard an uproar just outside the door,
So he leaped up to pull on his britches.

6. Says Brian McGurk, with a voice like a Turk,
    "Come, Paddy, and let us be eating. "
    Says big Andy Moore "We'll burst open the door.
    Sure this is no night to be waitin'."

7. The words were but spoke when the door it was broke,
    And they crowded 'round Paddy like leeches,
    And they swore by the hob if they didn't get grub
    They'd eat him clean out of his britches!

8. Poor Paddy in dread slipped up to the bed
    Where Judy, his wife, lay, God bless her,
    And soon, 'twas agreed that they should get a feed,
    So he took a big knife from the dresser.

9. Well, he cut out the waist of the britches, the beast,
    He tore off the buttons and stitches,
    Then he sliced them in stripes - just the way they do tripes-
    And made stew of his oul leather britches!

10. As they messed on the stuff, says Andy, "That's tough!"
    Says Brian, "You're no judge of mutton, "
    Then the same poor McGurk, on the point of a fork,
    Picked up a big ivory button!

11. Said Paddy, "What's that? Sure, I thought it ·ns fat."
    Brian leaped to his feet like a witch does;
    "Be the Powers above! I've been trying to shove
    Me teeth through the fly of his britches! "

12. Well, they all ran at Pat, who soon out of that.
    He flew when he saw them all rising.
    Says Brian "Make haste, and send for the priest:
    Be the blessed Saint Patrick, I'm poisoned! "

13. Revenge for the joke they had when they broke
    All the chairs and the tables and dishes,
    And from that very night they'd cut out your day-lights
    If they saw you with oul leather britches!

Oul Leather Britches 2

67

PATRICK LYNCH'S BOAT

Tune altered, words remade by Dominic Behan

On the deck of Pat-rick Lyn-ch's boat I sit in mourn-ful plight, With a sob-bing all the wea-ry day and a weep-ing all the night, If it was not for want and pov-er-ty from my coun-try forth-I-go By the bles-sed sun 'tis royal-ly I'd-sing thy-praise may-o.

2. When we did live in plenty and the gold did much abound,
In the company of fair young maids the Spanish ale went round
'Tis sad sad change from those gay days that I am forced to go,
I must sail away from Erin's Isle far from my own Mayo.

3. They are altered girls in Irrul now 'tis proud they've grown and high
With their hair-bags and their topknots for I pass their buckles by,
'Tis a bitter blow for me to go but God will have it so,
I must leave my bones in Santa Cruz far from my own Mayo.

4. It is my grief that Patrick Loughlin is not Earl in Irrul still,
Or that Brian Duff no longer rules as lord upon the hill,
Or that Colonel Hugh McGready should be dead and lying low
And me sailing swiftly sailing from the county of Mayo.

THE PATRIOT GAME

68

Words and music by Dominic Behan.

Come all you young re - bels and list while I sing

For love of one's land is a ter - rib - le thing

It ban - ish - es fear with the speed of a flame

and makes us all part of the pa - tri - ot game.

2. My name is O'Hanlon I'm just gone sixteen
   My home is in Monaghan there I was weaned
   I learned all my life cruel England to blame
   And so I'm a part of the Patriot Game.

3. It's barely a year since I wandered away
   With the local battallions of the bold I.R.A.
   I read of our heros and wanted the same
   To play up my part in the Patriot Game.

4. They told me how Connolly was shot in a chair
   His wounds from the fighting all bleeding and bare.
   His fine body twisted all battered and lame
   They soon made me part of the Patriot Game.

5. This Ireland of mine has for long been half-free
   Six Counties are under John Bull's Monarchy
   But still DeValera is greatly to blame
   For shirking his part in the Patriot Game.

6. I don't mind a bit if I shoot down police
   They are lackeys for war never guardians of peace,
   But at deserters I'm never let aim
   The rebels who sold out the Patriot Game.

7. And now as I lie with my body all holes,
   I think of those traitors who bargained and sold
   I'm sorry my rifle has not done the same
   For the Quislings who sold out the Patriot Game.

69
PAT AND THE GANGERMAN

Words by, and music adapted by Fintan Connolly

Says the gan-ger to me, "Oul friend" says he, as though we're life-long ma - ted "We must do things right for them that's white and them that's not should be ha - ted, - We must make sure that white and pure the best of jobs are tied for". Says I, "Would them jobs be the same ones be -god that I-rish-men could-n't ap - ply for? If yeh saw me in muck from head to foot you'd swear I was from Ni - ag - 'ra.

2.   "Oh Pat, says he, "Now that, " says he,
        "Is over and done with,
        "It's the sort of thing for remembering
        "We gangers were having fun with. "
        Says I, "Now guv, such signs of love
        "To me are nearly swaying.
        "It was lovely and grand to be shot by the Tans;
        "Is the next thing to me you'll be saying
        "If yeh saw me begod underneath a big hod
        "Yeh'd swear I was from Jamaica?"

3.   "Ah well, " says he, "To Hell, " says he,
        "With what has gone before yeh.
        "Yeh know, underneath this apparent concrete,
        "We secretly adore yeh. "
        "Yeh, do, " says I, "And that's no lie.
        "Your love is like contrition;
        "Your love is so great that you really do hate
        "To see me poor Country partitioned.
        "Look at me down a hole; you'd swear on your soul
        "That I had come from Rhodesia! "

4.   "Go away with your tricks for carrying bricks
        "Is what you do intend me,
        "If the Black and the White ever really unite
        "That day would surely end yeh.
        "There's not a man from any land
        "In these islands and beyond her,
        "But your policy was 'Devide them' because
        "Whoever devides them must conquer!
        "If yeh saw me and me friends digging under the Thames
        "Yeh couldn't tell me from them, sir! "

Pat and the Gangerman 2

70 THE PAWNSHOP

Parody on "Tipperary" by street children. New words and arrangement by Dominic Behan

2. If yer father's on the dole and food is very scarce,
    And there's not a thing to rob around the universe,
    Don't be down around the mouth the journey isn't long
    Just come along with me and shout our way down to the pawn.
    Chorus:

3. Every Monday mornin' yeh can see them sneakin' through,
    Using phoney monickers them that's well known to you,
    They'll jeer at your poor mother as she slopes off to the pawn,
    These oul wans with their graceful airs fur coats and no drawers on.
    Chorus:

© Copyright 1965, CODA MUSIC LIMITED.

POEM

Words and music by Dominic Behan

Very Freely

A sai-lor cour-ted a far-mer's daught-er Who lived con-ta-gious to the town of Stra-bane. With-love and me-lo-dy he did be-sought her -that she'd mar-ry him be-fore she'd mar-ry a-ny oth-er type or class-i-fi-ca-tion of a man, But the farm-er's daught-er had proud pos-sess-ions, one sil-ver tea-pot and two pounds ten in gold "Would you mar-ry me me bould salt wa-ter sail-or if I made them into a bundle and threw them into the bottom of the ocean cold?"

2.

I'd marry you me heart's conchantment, if you had nothing better than your oul wan's curse,
So she made a bundle of all her possessions and threw them into the bottom of the ocean cold,
That ends that verse.
But the sailor he could swim like a duckeen and diving into the water swam down deep below,
Brought up the bundle and came out chuckling, thinking of all the fun he'd have when he got
back to his home up on the hill on the side of Ballinasloe.

3.

But the farmer's daughter near killed herself laughing, there was nothing in that bundle
But an ould pitauneen of a stone,
A sailor courted a farmer's daughter, now he wishes he'd left her alone.

72

MY REDHEADED MOT
FROM RINGSEND

Words by, and tune adapted by Fintan Connolly

As I work down a hole here in Lon-don —
— For eight or nine days of each week —
— I think of my friends back in Ire-land, —
— And the oth-ers of whom I won't speak. —
— How I used to wan-der on Sun-day, —
— And me wa-ges on black port-er spend, —
— And then I would lie un-til Mon-day —
— With my red-head-ed * mot from Rings-end. —

* Mot – Dublin slang word for 'girl'.

© Copyright 1965, CODA MUSIC LIMITED,

2.   Down by the Basin I met her
        Standing alone by the North Wall
        And begod sure I'll never forget her
        For she wasn't a bit shy at all
        "Are yeh coming with me" but 'twas Sunday
        And I'd not like the Sabbath to bend
        So I said I would wait until Monday
        For my redheaded mot in Ringsend.

3.   Now here with me hand on me shovel
        And me pick drilling holes by the score
        The ganger's voice shouting out trouble
        But me thoughts they are on something more
        Far from the mixer and concrete
        My dreams of old Ireland all wend
        All hoping that soon I'll once more meet
        My redheaded mot in Ringsend.

4.   Oh an Irishman's home is his coffin
        For McAlpine or Richard Costain
        When they start you there's no sign of stoppin'
        Till they bury you down some old drain.
        Though my body and arms work like fury
        My mind always chooses to spend
        It's time far from foremen and worry
        With my redheaded mot in Ringsend.

My Redheaded mot from Ringsend 2

73

THE RAGMAN'S BALL

Words remade, new music by Wolfe Stephens

Just pay at-ten-tion for a while, my good friends one and
all, I'll sing to you a verse or two a-bout a fam-ous
ball. The ball was giv-en by some friends who lived down in Ashe
Street, In a cer-tain-part of the li-ber-ties where the rag-man used to meet.

2. When the names were called at seven o'clock every man was on the dot,
And to show respects to the manager, every ragman brought his mot;
I must say that I brought mine at twenty five minutes to eight,
And the first to stand up was Kieran Grace to tell me I was too late!

3. Then up jumps Humpy Soodelum, and he says "I think somehow
By the way you're goin' on all night you're lookini for a row,
But look here, Grace, if you want your face you'd better not shout or bawl;
There's a couple of hard chaws to be here tonight to respect the Ragman's ball. "

4. Then we all sat down to fish and chips, and every man was there,
And as a post of honour, Billy Boland took the chair.
He swiped the chair and sold it to an oul one in Carmen Hall,
And danced on the face of poor Kieran Grace the night of the Ragman's ball.

5. Says one, "You're a quare one, and Billy, you're hard to beat. "
When up jumps Liza Boland and told her to hold her prate;
My one made a clout at her, she missed and struck the wall,
And the two of them went in the ambulance the night of the Ragman's ball.

6. Just to make the thing a swell affair we all brought friends a few.
We brought up Tommy Reynolds and his old tin-whistle, too;
The gallant Jack Tar smoked his cigar and slipped coming through the hall,
He lost his bag and all his swag the night of the Ragman's ball.

7. For eating we had plenty, as much as we could hold.
We drank Brady's Loopline porter till around the floor we rolled.
Black eyes they were in great demand, not to mention split heads at all.
If anyone wants to commit suicide let him go to the Ragman's ball!

THE RIVER SILA

Adapted with new music from children's street song, by Wolfe Stephens

I know a wo-man and she lives in the woods wee-la wee-la wi-la I know a wo-man and she is no good down by the ri-ver Si-la She had a ba-by two months old wee-la wee-la wi-la She had a ba-by two months old down by the ri-ver Si-la.

2. She put the baby in the pond weela a weela a wila
She put it in with no clothes on down by the river Sila.
And when the baby she couldn't drown weela weela wila,
She bought a penknife in the town down by the river Sila.

3. She bought that penknife long and sharp weela weela wila,
And she stuck the penknife in the baby's heart down by the river Sila,
Two big polismen came knocking on the door weela weela wila
Two big polismen and two more down by the river Sila.

4. Did you stick a penknife in the baby's heart weela weela wila?
Yes I stuck a penknife in the baby's heart down by the river Sila.
They built a gallows high and bare weela weela wila,
And the cruel mother hangs up there down by the river Sila.

75 THE ROCKS OF BAWN

Arranged and adapted by Dominic Behan

Come all you lo-yal he - roes where - ev-er you may be, Don't - hire out to an - y mas - ter till you know what your work- may - be Don't hire out to an - y mas - ter or from the clear day light - till - dawn For he'll want you - to be ab - le - for to plough the rocks of Bawn.

2. My shoes they are well worn and the rain comes tumbling in,
    My auld coat sure it's threadbare now and I'm leaking to the skin,
    But I'll rise up in the morning drom the clear daylight to the dawn,
    And they'll want yeh to plough up the rocks of Bawn.

3   Me curse attend you Swiney* for yeh have me nearly robbed,
     You're sitting by the fireside with your feet upon the hob,
     You're sitting by the fireside from the clear day light till dawn,
     And yeh know yeh'll never be able to plough the rocks of Bawn.

4.   Oh rise up there lovely swiney and give yer horse some hay,
     And give him lots of good things to eat before you start the day,
     Don't feed him on soft turnip boy take him down to my green lawn,
     And then yeh might be able, to plough the rocks of Bawn.

5.   I wish that the Queen of England would write to me in time
     And put me in a regiment all in me youth and prime,
     I'd fight for Ireland's glory from the clear daylight till dawn,
     And I never would return to plough the rocks of Bawn.

* 1.   The White Rocks - considered by the satirist an impossible task,
                        but likely to be requested by the landowners.
* 2.   John Swiney -   Pronounced "Sweeney' - The author of the song.

The Rocks of Bawn 2

76

THE SAINT

New words and music by Dominic Behan from the singing of Stephen Behan

In Glen-da-lough lived an oul saint Who

spent all his days in aus - te-ri-ty. His man-ners were cu-ri-ous an'

quaint, He looked up - on girls with dis - pa-ri-ty Sing-ing

fol di de lol di de lay ri fol di di lol di di

lad- di ri fol di de lol di de lay - - ri

fol di de lol di de lad - di _____

2.   He was fond of reading a book
When he could get one to his wishes;
Fond of slinging his hook
Down among the young fishes;
Sing fol ------ etc:

3.   He went out fishing one day
An' landed a fine big trout, sir;
Kitty from over the way
Came to see what the Saint was about, sir;
Sing fol ------ etc:

4.   "Gat out of my sight." said the Saint,
"Don't ye know I'm a man of great piety?"
"My good manners I wouldn't taint
"By mixing in female society."
 Sing fol ------ etc:

5.   Kate wasn't goin' to give in,
And when he went home to his rockery
There she was seated within
Polishin' up his oul crockery;
Sing fol ------ etc:

6.   He gave the poor creature a shake,
I wish that a bobby had caught him;
He pushed her right into the lake,
And I swear that she sank to the bottom;
Sing fol ------ etc:

The Saint 2

77

THE SEA AROUND US

Tune is the old melody of " 'S faigamid siud mar a ta se".
Words by Dominic Behan.

They say that the lakes of Kil-lar-ney are fair That no
stream like the Lif-fey can ev-er com-pare, If it's wa-ter you want you'll find
no-thing more rare Than the stuff they make down by the o-cean —

CHORUS
The sea, oh the sea is the gradh geal mo croide,
Long may it stay be-tween Eng-land and me, It's a sure gua-ren-tee that some
hour we'll be free Oh! thank God we're sur-round-ed by wa-ter!

2.   Tom Moore made his waters meet fame and renown,
      A great lover of anything dressed in a crown;
      In brandy the bandy old Saxon he'd drown,
      But throw ne'er a one into the ocean.
      Chorus:

3.   The Scots have their whisky, the Welsh have their speech,
      And their poets are paid about tenpence a week
      Provided no hard words on England they speak;
      Oh Lord! What a price for devotion!
      Chorus:

4.   The Danes came to Ireland with nothing to do
      But dream of the plundered old Irish they slew;
      "Yeh will in your Vikings," said Brian Boru,
      And threw them back in the ocean!
      Chorus:

5.   Two foreign old monarchs in battle did join,
      Each wanting their head on the back of a coin:
      If the Irish had sense they'd both drown in the Boyne
      And Partitiion throw into the ocean!
      Chorus:

* Gradh geal mo croide:- great joy of my heart. Pronounced - Grah gyall muh cree.

The Sea Around Us 2

78

SEAN O'DWYER OF THE GLEN

Translated from the Irish and music adapted by Wolfe Stephens

As I rose in the morn-ing____ When the sum-mer sun was

shin-ing_____ I heard the hunts-man call - ing_____ And the

birds so sweet-ly sung, _____I saw the hare and bad-ger, ___ I

heard the long-billed wood-cock____ The sound up-on the ech-o ___ And the

loud shot of the guns, _____The fox was high up-on the grey rocks, Horse-men

shout-ing _____And a wo - man count-ing sad-ly of her geese, _____ But

now the wood has fal-len _____ Let us go a-cross the o-cean _____For

Sean O'Dui - ber a Glean-na____ The power has left your throne. _____

2. This my abiding sorrow, my shelter must be taken,
   The north wind knocks me over and death is in the skies,
   My goat, chained up and silent, no more delights the children,
   No more at noon must frolic or merry exercises,
   But there, the shaggy antlered stag, Lordly King,
   Upon the crag would live on furze until the last day of the world,
   Ah, could I get some respite from folk all high and noble,
   I'd sail across the ocean and leave my joys behind.

3. It's old I am and worried, half dead and all but buried,
   Still, living can't be hurried, the grave must wait it's turn,
   Before life came upon her I saw the flame grow stronger
   As the lamplight glowed the longer then the candle no more burns,
   The ones who were my children, gone, forbidden, their own ones ridding
   The wide world of my name,
   But it's home I ride in anguish for Royalty is banished
   Sean a Duiber a gleanna, you've finished with the game.

Sean a duiber a gleanna, - 'Sean, heir of the Glen / Sean O'Dwyer of the Glen.
                                    Pronounced- "Shawn a duueer a glanaa'.

117

79

SIT YEH DOWN
AND I'LL TREAT YEH DECENT

New words and new music by Dominic Behan

2. I've travelled East and I've travelled westwards
From Manhattan Island to County Clare,
And wherever I went I sure knew a welcome
Was always waiting to greet me there.
Chorus:

3. Hard work they say since first invented,
Has never killed and that's the plan
To wed with work like love contented
But not Muldoon the solid man.
Chorus:

4. When I am dead and in my placing,
Sing songs and stories of rhyme and rann
But let them say when my life they're tracing,
"Here lies Muldoon, the solid man."

THE SEAN BEAN BOCT

Words and music adapted by Wolfe Stephens

"Oh the French are on the sea," - says - the sean bean boct, "Yes the French are on the sea," - says - the sean bean boct. - "The French are in the bay they'll be here with-out de - lay, And the Eng - lish will de - cay" - Says - the sean bean boct "Yes the Eng-lish will de - cay," - says - the sean bean boct.

2. "This England does quite well" says the Sean Bean Boct.
  "This England does quite well" says the Sean Bean Boct.
  "This England does quite well, in murder she excels,
  "But of course she learned in Hell," says the Sean Bean Boct.
  "But of course she learned in Hell," says the Sean Bean Boct.

3. "What culture does she boast?" says the Sean Bean Boct,
  "What culture does she boast?" says the Sean Bean Boct.
  "The culture that she boasts is to see a freeman roast,
  "And serve liberty on toast" says the Sean Bean Boct
  "And serve liberty on toast" says the Sean Bean Boct.

4. "Can we ever then be free?" says the Sean Bean Boct.
  "Can we ever then be free?" says the Sean Bean Boct.
  "Yes Ireland will be free from the centre to the sea,
  "When comes the time for liberty," says the Sean Bean Boct,
  "When comes the time for liberty," says the Sean Bean Boct.

*Sean Bean Boct, Poor Old Woman a code name for Ireland, Shan Van Vocht.

81

SLEEP MY LOVE

Translated from the Gaelic with new music by Fintan Connolly

Sho - heen sho-ho my won-der-ful trea-sure, my share of this world my sleep smil-ing boy. How grand my de-light, how big is my plea-sure to crad-le you so is my great-est of joys. Sweet child of my heart, sleep on with-out sor-row, For-tune and health lie be - fore you I know. No - cares there to meet you, a hap - py to -mor- row will be there to greet you, sho - heen, sho-heen sho.

2. On Mullachaseedy* the fairies are staying,
   The fair moon of Spring playing down on their games;
   And here they come calling for you to go straying
   To leave my heart empty where once my child reigned.
   Their tricks and their music shall never entice you
   'Though sweeter than Pan are the whistles they blow,
   I'm here at your cof and I'm praying beside you
   They never shall lure you, shoheen, shoheen sho.

3. Down from above the angels are peeping
   Kindly, with love, but inviting you there,
   And their home would we grandeur if they had you sleeping
   Where Heaven could lavish Her love on my care.
   But here by your Mammy, sweet child be my treasure,
   God does not grudge me my darling I know,
   For he'd not want to see his fair Angels in pleasure
   While I'd live in sorrow, shoheen shoheen sho.

* MulacantSide: - "The Hill Of Side' - Pronounced - "Mullachaseedy'.

SLIAB NA MBAN

Translated with new music by Wolfe Stephens.

My heart - is bro - ken in _____ sor - row a to _____
ken _____ of re - gret for jeers now spo-ken by the Eng-lish
lords _____ They knew we could do no harm for - they knew we pos-sess'd - no
arms _____ But - forks and pikes and but a hand-ful of rust-ed
swords. _____ We had no ma - jor no he - ro lea - der, No man - to
or - der us we drif-ted on. _____ Like cows to a dro - ver e'er _____ the
fair - is o _____ ver _____ we - scat - ter'd on the
sun - ny should - ers of Sliab Na Mban. _____

2.   But the French are waiting their masts are straining and people
They are saying they sail the sea
With their ships in serried lines and their order is grand and fine
And they race against the wind to set old Ireland free.
Now if I knew this tale was true, I'd sing like the blackbird for you a happy song,
To see broken ranks swinging and hear French trumpets ringing as Freedom
they come bringing to Sliab na mBan.

* Sliab na mBan: The White Mountains. Pronounced: Sleeve na Maun

© Copyright 1965, CODA MUSIC LIMITED.

83

SMITH OF BRISTOL

Words and tune altered by Dominic Behan.

Smith was a Bris-tol man and a rare old sort was he, With his cut-lass and his pis-tols heave ye ho! ___ With a no-ble crew of cut-throats he used to scour the sea, A-plund-'ring and a rob-bing high and low. ___ He swore 'twas no con-cern - he did-n't give a darn - A-bout right or wrong or a-ny ho-ly show ___ He swore that grab and boo-ty was Bri-tain's fore-most du-ty Where-ev-er she could get it heave ye ho! ___

CHORUS: Heave ye ho! Heave ye ho! Heave ye ho! ___ He swore that grab and boo-ty was Bri-tain's fore-most du-ty, Where-ev-er she could get it, heave ye ho! ___

2. Smith had a noble soul, and lofty was his pride;
    With his cutlass and his pistols heave ye ho!
    He'd watch his beaten foreman jump out into the tide
    Call "Ye beggars, you had nowhere else to go!"
    And hanging from his lanyard were Portuguese and Spaniards
    And beaten Frenchmen jumping to and fro!
    Right along the blazing story shone allume in England's glory:
    Pirate Smith of Bristol, heave ye ho!
    Chorus:

3. But accidents will happen even to heroes such as he,
    With his cutlass and his pistols heave ye ho!
    He was standing at his capstan as happy as could be
    Hoping soon to have another prizing foe
    When a whistling Spanish bullet came and caught him in
                                            the gullet,
    And, very sad to say, it laid him low;
    He was only ninety-seven, but his soul is gone to Heaven
    To rest on Nelson's bosom, heave ye ho!
    Chorus:

Smith of Bristol 2

84

THE SODDING

Words by, and music adapted by Fintan Connolly

Were yeh ev - er a - bove on the glas - ne - vin bend when the
wind cut your face and the rain would-n't end And the corp-ses stood up and they
gave three hur-rahs for they thought yeh were com-in' to join them at last? I'll
tell yeh no lie, tho' that ce-me-t'ry sleeps it al-ways be-jaz-es fills
me with the creeps, Es - pecial - ly when up to a
sod-ding I roam And a voice some-where whis-pers "Yer not go - in' home."

2.   Then some clergyman kicks up a bloody loud din
     When he gets them singin' some mournful ould hymn,
     And the silence is shook when he throws a few clods
     Of turf on the top of the boxed-in poor sod.
     Then out with the hankies and dryin' of eyes,
     "I loved him!" "Adored him!" All bloody lies:
     They think they'll not quick enough be from the joint
     To get to the 'Brian Boru' bar for a pint!

3.   With their small ones and large ones, the greedy oul things,
     Some hypocrite says "Now he'd like to sing;
     "A man of the world he'd never see wrong
     If we cheered ourselves up with a bar of a song."
     Then the widow she manfully tales off her cant,
     "I'm sure that it's what Johnny would want,"
     And though she controls every muscle, the bitch,
     Her feet below table are starting to twitch.

4.   Well, talk about mourners beginning to sing,
     Before long they're prancing and dancing the Fling;
     There's a rush to the counter with fivers and pounds,
     And Johnny, as usual's, out of the round.
     Then some drunk 'round the widow places an arm
     Tryin' to console her, and meanin' no harm,
     When some narky relation, made brave on the stout,
     Into the street he invites the man out!

5.   The widow, she screams - to get into the act -
     "For God's sake; For Johnny's sake hold them two back!
     "If Johnny could see the disgrace to his name
     "The poor man, bejazes, would die of the shame!"
     If you're thinkin' of dying now take my advice;
     If yer thinkin' of dying in Dublin think twice.
     Hang on till this crowd gets their call to appear,
     Unless yeh want them to make the joke of the year.

The Sodding 2

85 SONG FROM THE BACKWOODS

Arranged and adapted from the original of Timothy Daniel Sullivan by Dominic Behan.

2. We've heard her faults a hundred times, the new ones and the old,
   In songs and sermons, rants and rhymes enlarged a thousand-fold;
   But hear them all, the great and small, and list to what we say;
   Here's to Ireland! Loved old Ireland! Ireland, boys, hurray!
   Chorus:

3. We know that brave and good men tried to snap her rusty chain,
   That rebels suffered, tortured, died, and snivellers cried "In vain!"
   But oh, boys, oh, a glance will show how far they've won the day;
   Here's to Ireland! Loved old Ireland! Ireland, boys, hurray!
   Chorus:

4. But deep in Canadian woods we've met, and we may not see again
   The dear Isle where our hearts are set, where our fond hopes remain;
   But let it pass, come drink the glass, and with each drop we'll say
   Here's to Ireland! Grand old Ireland! Ireland, boys, hurray!
   Chorus:

THE SOUTH DOWN MILITIA

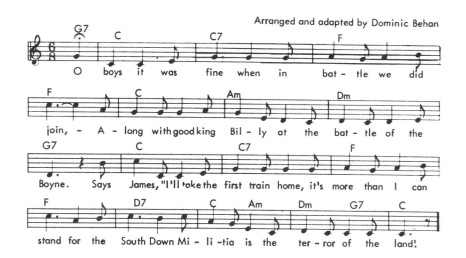

Arranged and adapted by Dominic Behan

O boys it was fine when in bat - tle we did join, - A - long with good king Bil - ly at the bat - tle of the Boyne. Says James, "I'll take the first train home, it's more than I can stand for the South Down Mi - li -tia is the ter - ror of the land!

2.   You may talk about your Queen's Guards, Scots Greys and all;
You may rave about your Kilties and your gallant Forty-Two,
Or any other regiment under the Kings Command,
But the South Down Militia is the terror of the land! (Chorus).

3.   When we went up to London in September sixty-two
The King and Queen and dukes were there parading for review:
"O Blood and Thunder! " says the Queen,
As she waved her lily-white hand,
"Sure the South Down Militia is the terror of the land!(Chorus).

4.   When Kruger heard the regiment was landed at Capetown
"De Wet" says he, "We're beat! " says he, "They've sent out the South Down;
And De Wet, me boyo, that is true, we'll have to leave the Rand,
For the South Down Militia is the terror of the land! "(Chorus).

5.   When we went out ot Flanders to fight the awful Hun
The Kaiser said to old Van Kluck "The war is nearly done!
I never thought the Orange Drum would beat the German Band;
Oh, the South Down Militia is the terror of the land! "(Chorus).

6.   When the Sultan heard the regiment was at the Dardanelles
He rushed out of his harem and gave three awful yells -
"Allah, Allah save us. Oh save us or we're damned,
For the South Down Militia is the terror of the land! "(Chorus).

87

THE SPINNING WHEEL SONG

Words and music by John Francis Waller, LL.D.

Mel-low the moon-light to shine is be-gin-ning,_____ Close by the win-dow young Ei-leen is spin-ning, ___ Bent o'er the fire her blind grand-moth-er's sit-ting_____ Groan-ing and moan-ing and drow-si-ly knit-ting,_____ "Ei-leen, I sure-ly - hear some-bo-dy tap-ping?" "'Tis the i-vy, dear Moth-er, a-gainst the glass flap-ping." "Ei-leen, a ca-ra - I hear some-one sigh-ing," -"'Tis the sound mo-ther dear,of the Aut-umn wind die-ing."

CHORUS

Mer-ri-ly, cheer-i-ly noi-si-ly whir-ring, Swings the wheel, spins the wheel,while the foot's stir-ring, Spright-ly and light-ly, and air-i-ly ring-ing Thrills the sweet voice of the young maid-en sing-ing._____

2. "What's that noise that I hear at the window, I wonder?"
    " 'Tis the little bird chirping, the holly bush under."
    "What makes you keep shoving and moving your stool on
    "And singing all wrong the old song of the Coolun?"
    There's a form at the casement - the form of her true love,
    And he whispers, with face bent, "I'm waiting for you, love.
    "Get up on the stool, through the lattice step lightly;
    "We'll rove through the grove while the moon's shining brightly."
    Chorus:

3. The maid shakes her head, on her lips lays a finger,
    Steals up from the seat - longs to go, but yet lingers,
    A frightened glance turns to her drowsy Grandmother,
    Puts one foot on the stool, spins the wheel with the other.
    Lazily, easily, swings now the wheel round.
    Slowly and lowly is heard now the reel's sound.
    Noiseless and light to the lattice above her
    The maid steps, then leaps to the arms of her lover.

Final Chorus:
    Slower, and slower, and slower the wheel swings;
    Lower, and lower, and lower the reel rings.
    Ere the reel and the wheel stopped their ringing and moving
    Through the grove the young lovers by moonlight are roving.

*   A cara: 'My Friend' - Pronounced 'A kaura.'

*   'The Coolun' - A sixteenth century folk song
                about a girl with fair hair - 'An Chuil-fhionn'.

The Spinning Wheel Song 2

88

THERE CAME THREE JEWS

Children's street song arranged and adapted by Dominic Behan

THREE FARMERS FROM THE NORTH

Arranged and adapted by Wolfe Stephens

Oh there were three far-mers from the north and they were pass-ing by - They each swore out a might-y oath that bar-ley corn-must die - One of them said drown him and the oth-er said hang him high, For who-ev-er will stick to the bar-ley grain a beg-gin' he will die Yes who-ev-er shall stick to the bar-ley grain a beg-gin' he will die.

2. They put John Barley in a sack on a cold and wintry day,
   They brought him to a pottery and burned him in the clay,
   Frost and snow began to melt before the job was done
   When Barley grain scratched his oul brain saying "Hello me darling sons"
   Yes Barley grain scratched his oul brain "Hello me darlin' sons."

3. Yeh'd want to see him in the Summer when the harvest's comin' on,
   There he stands up in the field like a great big hairy man,
   The reaper cetts him with his hook and pulls him barbarously,
   In the middle he grabs him like a crook and cuts above the knee.
   In the middle he grabs him like a crook and cuts above the knee.

4. The binder then the thrasher comes to flail him to the bones,
   You can almost hear old Barley's sighs and grunts and moans,
   Then they get the poor oul thing and throw him into a well,
   They leave him there for a day and a night until he starts to swell.
   They leave him there for a day and a night until he starts to swell.

5. The barley grain is a comical thing when it dies it makes men laugh,
   For they soon forget their worries when they've little more than a glass,
   The drunkard uses Barley grain the very worst of all,
   He drinks him down with a nasty frown and waters the garden walls,
   Yes he drinks him down with a nasty frown and waters the garden walls.

90

TO DIE FOR IRELAND

Words and music by Wolfe Stephens

To die for Ire - land was I born with_____ ven-gence in my birth, My mo-ther showed me how to shu.. the plea-sures of this earth. The danc-ing and the hur-ling team I learned to pass them by To vin- di - cate a mo - ther's- spleen for Ire-land I must die a stor for Ire-land I must die, For moun-tain streams and re-bel's dreams for Ire-land I must die.

2. All would I give could I but live to see her people free
For rocks and stones and rebel bones yearn not for liberty,
With slogans bold her sons are told humanity pass by.
Compared to land what worth has man but for that land to die a stor?*
But for that land to die,
That vision grand is Motherland for Ireland I must die.

3. And as I see my brothers he enchained in bonds of toil
They ask me then to forget the men who would my kin despoil,
The men who own this land of mine for that my life would give
The glory ours to them the power and all their faults forgive a stor
And all their faults forgive,
I will not die for them a stor but for my brothers live.

*A stor, My treasure Pronounced A Store.

THE TWANGMAN'S REVENGE

Arranged with new words by Dominic Behan

Come-lis-ten to-me sto-ry It's a-bout-a nice young man- When the Mi-li-tia was-n't wan-tin' he dealt in haw-kin' twang-He loved a pret-ty fair-maid as fair as a-ny midge,- Who kept a trea-cle Bil-ly de-pot one side of the Car-lisle bridge.

2. Another one came courtin' her, his name was Micky Bags,
He was a commercial traveller he dealt in bones and rags,
He took her out to Sandymount to see the waters roll
And won the heart of the twangman's girl playin' billy in the Bowl.

3. Now when the twangman heard of this he flew into a terrible rage,
And he swore by the contents of his twang cart on him to have revenge,
He watched them lark in the Phoenix Park and swore through gritted teeth,
Tonight I'll bite with my long knife revenge they say is sweet.

4. He knew the route the Bags would use along up Watling Hill,
His heart it pounded like a flute he told it to be still,
He lay in wait by James' Gate and when poor Bags come up
With his long knife he took the life of the porr oul gatherem up.

92

THE TIP'RARY RECRUIT

Wolfe Stephen's words and music.

Me love was a sol-dier no sold-ier was bold-er than

my love when no old-er than sweet sev-en-teen, But they took a Fi-

ga-ry one morn-ing quite ear-ly to take him from Ti-pe-ra-ry to

fight for the Queen. "Her ma-jest-y bless her", as he did ad-dress her with

words he car-ess'd her like jol-ly John Brown, "Dis-rae-li has said how you're

mak-ing your bed Now far off now in-stead now in black-est Cape-Town."

2. "Goodbye bonny whore will yeh open the door? I'll give them bloody Boers what the why and what for,"
Well before yeh could speak now in less than a week now he'd an arm and half cheek now behind in the war.
Well, Heaven's above him God Bless him and love him, out I'd never shove him for loss of an arm,
But he got a one made from the shaft of a spade and when wound up it played loud the Soldier's Alarm.

3. In bed of a night sure I'd get such a fright, when me man came home tight and forgot to switch out,
The arm half sober, would roll me all over and out of the clover I'd fall with a clout.
If me fella got bumped the ould arm took the hump and handed out thumps be you polis or pure,
And if it wanted for walkin' there was no use in talkin' it just started hawkin' yeh out through the door.

4. Well, at last 'twas agreed that the arm did need a mate for its greed so we made a male limb,
But when it was fitted before it had knitted said the arm half witted "sure I am him."
"God bless us and save us" says Mrs. Kate Davis, "a lather and shave us as quick as yeh can!"
The arms became lovers and Heavens above her ran off with each other around me old man.

The Tip'rary Recruit 2

93

TRUST IN DRINK

Based freely by Dominic Behan on a free translation
from the Irish "Preab san Ol" by Brendan Behan

2. Ther's them that's with us, sour and religious, who, quite prodigious
   would bid us hold;
   Count every penny, do not spend any, be dry and canny and mind
   your gold.
   Chorus:

3. When sorrow binds you and salt tears blind you hard drink will mind you
   and ease your grief,
   Gay dissipation is worth the making get down to taking some wet relief.
   Chorus:

4. There's many head men and quite well-fed men and quite well dead men
   in six by four,
   And before this chorus is half-way o'er us under the clovers there'll be
   plenty more.
   Chorus:

WALK MY LOVE

Translation by Wolfe Stephens

I wish I was on yon-der hill it's there I'd sit and weep my fill, And oh, the tears would ming-le still oh may he be pro-tec ——— ted well. Walk – walk – walk my love, walk with grace and soft-ly move Walk thru' that door and give me joy my own-one my soft-spo-ken boy.

2. I'll sell my rock I'll sell my reel
   I'll sell my cloth and spinning wheel
   To buy for my love a sword of steel
   Oh may he be protected well.
   Chorus:

3. Now that my love to France has gone
   And left me here to weep alone
   All my salt tears will turn to stone
   Oh may he be protected well.
   Chorus:

4. Oh God I wish, but that's all vain
   No one to hear as I complain,
   Oh Mother, send he is not slain
   Oh may he be protected well.
   Chorus:

95

THE WAXIE'S DARGLE

New words and music by Dominic Behan.

Says my oul wan to your oul wan "Will yeh come to the wax-ies dar-gle?" "Says your oul wan to my oul wan "Sure I have-n't got a farth-in' I've just been down to Mon-to Town to see un-cle Mc-Ar-dle, He would-n't lend me a half a crown for to go to the wax-ie's darg-le."

2,   "Take off yer coat and Paisley shawl and put them in the pawn, mam,
      "And if yeh get a coin at all we'll have a one and one mam,
      "For by the water Guiness flows as free as the river's gargle,
      "To poverty, mam thumb yer nose and come to the Waxie's Dargle."

3.   The Dargle is a stream so fair all flowing through old Bray, sir,
      Five miles from Monto it lies there, so near and far away sir,
      The candle-makers all unite as did before their Fathers,
      For one whole day and half the night to enjoy the Waxie's Dargle.

THE WEARING OF THE GREEN

Arranged and adapted by Fintan Connolly

Oh — Pad-dy dear and did you hear the news that's go - ing round, The sham-rock is by law for-bid to grow on I-rish ground, No man Saint Pat-rick's Day shall keep his co-lour can't be seen For there's a cruel - law a-gainst the wear - ing of the green. I met with Nap-per Tan - dy and he took me by the hand, Said he"How is old Ire - land and how does she stand?" "She's the most dis-tress-ful coun - try that ev-er could be seen, For they're hang-ing men and wo-men for the wear-ing of the green."

2. Then since the colour we must wear is England's cruel red,
No Irishman must now forget the blood that has been shed,
They may take the shamrock from our breasts and cast it on the sod,
But it will take root where'er it rests though underfoot it's trod,
When the law can stop the blades of grass from growing as they grow,
And when the leaves in Summertime their colours daren't show,
Then I'll take down the shamrock that I wear on Paddy's e'en,
But until that day I'll live and die still wearing of the green.

97 WHEN I'M TWENTY

Words & Music by Dominic Behan

I've been a teen-ag-er for ma-ny a year and me dad-dy keeps say-in' me clothes is all queer, me hair's so un-ti-dy, dear dad is ap-palled_____ but that's on-ly be-cause my dear dad-dy is bald. But when I-'m twen-ty_____ not a mo-ment be-fore I will be a teen-ag-er no nev-er_____ no more._____ Dear more.

2. I'm not like dear dad
When dear daddy was young
I've no int'res't at all in
Tanks, bullets or guns
A dance or a song are the
Things that I like, and my
Old fighter plane is a
New motor-bike,
But when I'm twenty, etc. –

3. I know nothing of glory in
Far foreign parts, the only
Battle I know is the fight
In the charts, I'm a
Dreamer, a Beatle, but
When my hair's grown, I'll give
Five of the best to the
Bold Rolling Stones,
But when I'm twenty, etc. –

YEH MEN OF SWEET LIBERTIES HALLS

New Music. Words adapted by Dominic Behan

2. Let us sing of the Coombe and each street, before the vile Union was known,
   When the Lords and the Ladies did meet and around it a glory had thrown,
   Then high were Newmarket and Court, the Poddle, the Chamber the Manor,
   Where thousands each day did resort placing trade on the Liberties banner.

3. There was New Street and Sweet Warrenmount Faddle Alley and oul Blackpitts
   But give to them their full account, for it's there that I made me best hits
   There was John Street Cork Street and Mill Street and the various alleys and lanes,
   And Marrowbone Lane ever sweet where strong water for ever more reigns.

4. At Echlin Street Harbour I saw comin' down the wide mighty canal,
   More and many an oul sober craw and scores of me own drunken pals,
   Though blind in the sight of me eyes I pray never to see Fumbally Lane,
   For of every oul street 'neath the skies it's there dwelt dirty Dickie McGrane.

99

YOUNG JOHNNY IS MINE

Words and music by Wolfe Stephens

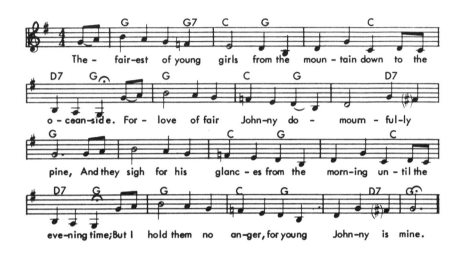

The - fair-est of young girls from the moun - tain down to the
o - cean-side. For - love of fair John-ny do - mourn - ful-ly
pine, And they sigh for his glanc - es from the morn-ing un - til the
eve-ning time; But I hold them no an-ger, for young John-ny is mine.

2. At the drinking or dancing no one man his peer could ever be,
   At the football he stands like Horatio of old;
   And when we meander the young girls they turn to sneer at me
   For tonight, in his arms, me young Johnny will hold.

3. Oh my love for young Johnny burns madly inside my breast,
   It's flame never dims and my heart's never free
   But though sweet be the love that keeps moving my heart's unrest,
   Ah, sweeter by far is my love's love for me.

THE
ZOOLOGICAL GARDENS

New words and music by Dominic Behan

CHORUS:

Thun-der and light-nin' it's - no lark when Dub - lin
ci - ty is in the dark, Would yeh care - to go to the
Phoe-nix Park and view the zoo - log - i - cal gard - ens?

VERSE

I went up there on me ho - ney - moon we saw the
lions and the ould - ba - boon, And we strayed for a while 'neath the
sil - v'ry moon a - round the zoo - log - i - cal gar - dens.

Chorus:
2. She says to me, me dear friend, Jack, sure I'd like a ride on the elephant's back,
   If yeh don't go outa that I'll give you such a smack around the zoological gardens.

Chorus:
3. But Jack, says she to give you yer due, there's nothin' jumps around as well as you,
   No not even the big Australian kangaroo around the zoological gardens.

Chorus:
4. Oh Lord says I now don't be daft, she says it's true and yer not to laugh,
   But yer lovely and long like the spotted giraffe, up in the zoological gardens.

Chorus:
5. We left by the gate at Castleknock, she says me dear sure we'll court on the lock,
   Then I knew she was one of the rare oul stock outside the zoological gardens.
   Chorus:

"IRELAND SINGS": AN ANTHOLOGY OF MODERN AND ANCIENT IRISH SONGS

1. A BRAVE NEW WORLD:
   A song of hope for the future.

2. AN RAIB TU AG AN g CARRIG?
   Nationalism and Catholicism were proclaimed by the English in Ireland, so they became synonymous to a great number of people until after Catholic Emancipation, when the attitude of the clergy in relation to the struggle changed. During the Penal days in Ireland, images of the Virgin had to be hidden from the attentions of the English military crusaders. This song, about such a hiding place has been freely translated from the Irish.

3. A NATION ONCE AGAIN:
   COMMUNICATION is a military weapon in times of war and unrest. The idea of disseminating revolutionary ideology through song became, in Ireland, if not a fine, certainly a prolific art. No country on earth has so many good and bad National songs. And yet, because it is so premeditated in its poetic pretensions, "A Nation Once Again" is probably less a 'Folk' song than the very much inferior "Kevin Barry".

4. A POUND FOR TO LEND:
   A good description for how history is handed down in many Irish homes.

5. AS I WAS GOING O'ER THE MOOR
   An 'art' song, but none the worse for that.

6. BAD LUCK TO THE MARCHING:
   One of the earliest jibes about discipline in the British Army. At first sight, it seems a sensible move to swell the ranks of the conquerer from the homes of the conquered. In the long run, however, it doesn't work, as could be seen in the men coming back on leave from the British Army to use their British rifles on English troops during the 1916 Rising. Egypt, India, and Africa are following suit, and maybe even Scotland and Wales will get a few ideas.

7. BALLAD OF OLIVER ST. JOHN GOGARTY, THE
   Gogarty, the Poet-Surgeon, is probably better known throughout the world for his part in 'Ulysses' as Buck Mulligan, than as a Free State Senator arrested by the I.R.A. during the Republican campaign. Friend of W.B. Yates, and A.E. Russell, he was a fine boxer, but there is no record of his having fought outside the ring.

8. BONNY BUNCH OF ROSES, THE
   A County Tyrone Ballad of Napoleon and his Mother.

9. BOOLAVOGUE:

Said to have been composed by Miles Byrne, who died afterwards in Exile.
Byrne held that Father John Murphy, the hero of the art song, "Boolavogue",
advised his flock to take no part in the 1798 Rebellion, and only joined the
fight after his chapel and house had been burned by the Yeomanry. P.J.
Macall's version of the battle, and how Father Murphy led the fight from beginning to end, is much more popular in Ireland than this, the original.

10. BOY FROM WEXFORD, THE

The cropped head, singling out known rebels from the rest of the Irish people,
became a badge of honour after '98. This song of defiance is more typical of
the Irish spirit, than the mealy mouthed slushy sentimental "Croppy Boy" which
begins, "Good men and true in this house who dwell", which song has only
one thing to recommend it - the description of an English officer dressed in
priest's garb in an effort to use the confessional as an intelligence agency.
The English did all that and more.

11. BOSS ALAS, THE

I worked one time on a building scheme with a man who was, to me, a potential
scab. He was always on the job before anybody else, nor did he leave until
after everybody else. The boss himself - oh, a sweet thing in a child's frock -
came once a day and spoke to nobody but this one man, and yet on Friday,
the most militant men were always sacked. I met him some weeks after they
had given me the push, and he was drinking in a pub during working hours.
I asked him if he wasn't afraid of losing his job, and he replied, "The old
bastard is dead, and there's nobody to take his place until after the funeral".
Hence this song.

12. BRIAN O'LYNN

One of the best known nursery rhymes. Tam O'Linn, Geordie O'Linn, Jock
O'Linn, agaus olainn againnse, and that's where it might have derived from,
'Ol', drink. The super optimist - badly needed just now.

13. BROWN AND YELLOW ALE, THE

Tale of a man who loses his wife because he becomes impotent through too much
drinking. Mrs. Costello gives another version of this theme in her collection
"Amrain Muige Seola", but here drinking is not held responsible. "Brown and
Yellow Ale" was freely translated by the poet, James Stephens.

14 BUTCHER OF GLOUCESTER D, THE

When I was a kid, the two biggest rival gangs in Dublin were the Ash Street
gang from the southside, and the Animal gang from Gloucester Diamond on the
north. Most of the abbatoirs of the northside were situated in and around the
'Diamond' and irate men were not particularly selective in their choice of
weapons.

15   BROWN THORN BUSH, THE

In Irish, "An Droigneार Donn", translated from the version in "Hardiman's Irish Minstrelsy" Vol.1. "The Kerry Boatman" is obviously another version of the same song.

16.   CARRICROE

During the famine of 1845/47, the people of Ireland were almost starved out of existence by Victoria. The gracious Queen sent a cheque for five pounds as a contribution towards feeding the then population of close on nine millions. Lest people got the idea in England that she was weakening in her politics towards the Irish, her majesty sent by the same post a cheque for the same amount to Battersea Dogs' Home. The population of Ireland today is somewhat around four millions.

17.   CASTLE OF DRUMBOE, THE

During the Civil War in Ireland, 1921/1923, four men were shot by Free State Forces in circumstances similar to the murder of Patrice Lumumba and his adjutants in the Congo.

18.   CHILD WEDDING:

'I married was, alas, a high lady to be', and again, 'If better be more fit, I'll send him to the court awhile to point his pretty wit'. Compare with that English Elizabethan version, the Scots 'The trees are a' ivy the leaves they are green, The time is lang past that I hae seen', and you'll see the terrible things go on when the drawingroom tries to get nearer the kitchen, in rooms that is. Match making, young women to old men usually, but the Irish version does an about face, after all we're not going to show our girls in a bad light.

19.   CHEER UP RUSSELL STREET:

I was born in Russell Street, Dublin, and this is one of the many songs sung by Dublin kids. Of course the same song has been used for many streets too; cheer up Mercer Street, York Street, Cuffe Street and the Coombe. Sometime ago it was picked up by an East End Cockney living in Glasgow who promptly adapted it to become "Cheer Up Celtic!" (Celtic and Rangers are the two principal and rivalling Glasgow Soccer Football Clubs).

20.   COME ALL YOU BRAVE UNITED MEN:

The Catholic Church banned Free-Masonry because of its secret nature. When it suited certain Bishops they banned Republican movements too, alleging the same reasons. This song is reputed to have been written by O'Donovan Rossa, one of the last of the great Fenians of 1867. Of the Fenians, Dr. Moriarity, Bishop of Kerry wrote, "Hell is not hot enough, nor Eternity long enough to roast (them)".

21. **CONNAUGHT RANGERS, THE**

When news of the 1916 Rising reached the Connaught Rangers stationed in India, many of the men mutinied.

22. **CROOKED JACK:**

Eamonn Smullen, a good Republican Socialist, worked on the Hydro' Electric scheme in Inverary, Scotland. He described the conditions under which the men worked as appalling.

23. **DICEY RILEY:**

Joyce's 'Nightgown' sequence in 'Ulysses' deals with quite a few of the ladies mentioned in this song. My aunt sings a version about Biddy Riley. What the hell, Biddy, Maggie, or what have you. Some unfortunate now past her labour and ready to give her back a rest.

24. **DIRTY LANE:**

M.J. MORAN'S invective finding its target full head on. Most of Moran's songs existed in scraps, as did the songs of Johnny Brady, John Martin, and Richie Madden. About fifteen or twenty years ago I started 'restoring' them. I must have succeeded somewhat because I heard lately in Dublin the "Dubliners" singing "The Twangman's Revenge" which I recorded for Topic records in 1956. I beg nobody's pardon for this, because my Mother says, "If I don't like a line, dear, or I've just forgotten it, I make up my own". Joe Heaney, the great Galway singer told Karl Dallas, "When the line is short I can add some decorations, when it's long I can't". And there you have the dialectical development of folk music.

25. **DOWN IN YONDER MEADOW:**

Children's street song.

26. **DUBLIN FUSILIERS, THE**

Never heard anything but the chorus of this. Thought it deserved better treatment, so there.

27. **EXILES:**

Brendan Behan's favourite tune. He used to plague Barney McKenna and Ronnie Drew to play it for him. Didn't have words to speak of before now.

28. **THE FAIR TORMENTOR:**

"Funeral Wake", says he, "sure aren't all wakes funereal?" Well, there's the hiring wake that went on in the 12th century and there's the American Wake going on even now, that's the time when people say "Is he dead?" and they're told, "Well, not exactly, but he's gone to Boston". From the singing of Seamus Bawn Conneely this has been translated.

V

29. FINEEN THE ROVER:

People laugh nowadays at Ireland's maritime effort. But there was a time, and not so long ago (archaeologically anyway), when the Irish Rover was a match for five Romans, or twenty if they were English ones. Indeed it's said that the name Nelson was originally O'Neill. Drake of course, comes from the Irish 'O Droicead' meaning 'of the bridge', while Blithe is 'Blatain' or 'The Little Flower'.

30. FINNEGAN'S WAKE:

From the Wake of Tim Finnegan, James Joyce starts the stream of conciousness that has wrapped the literary world in sleepless confusion ever since. Take away the possessive quality of the noun by simply removing the apostrophe and you have a great war cry to all the sons of Finn McCool, "Finnegans, Wake!"

31. GET ME DOWN ME PETTICOAT

The Linen Hall, off Bolton Street, Dublin, was the depot from where the British Army paid dependents of their troops recruited from Ireland. If a chap wanted to spite his wife, he would go to fight the Boers under another name.

32. HOW CAESER WAS DRIVEN FROM IRELAND:

When the Irish are short of a foreign oppressor with whom to fight, they sit around the pubs gritting their teeth and inventing Englishmen.

33. IRISH ASTRONOMY:

Saint Patrick drove the snakes from Ireland and they all became American business men.

34. JOE BRADY:

Brendan Behan collected this song from Mrs. Mary Fitzimmons and the song 'speaks' for Itself.

35. JOHNNY I HARDLY KNEW YEH:

One of the great anti-war songs. Ireland, like all revolutionary countries, maintains paradoxical attitudes to war and peace. The reasons are not so recondite, because revolutions are fought for a bit of peace from oppression.

36. JOIN THE BRITISH ARMY:

This song gave my Father a fierce headache in 1934. Brendan jeeringly sang it in the wake of two fine stalwart 'Skins' - Enniskillen Fusiliers, and got a clip on the ear, while my Father was passing by. He would have beaten the two of them without sweatin' had they not taken to their heels. On his way in the door in the heat of the aftermath of battle, he banged his head on the lintel. And it must have been an extraordinary door because me Da is only five feet three.

37. **KERRY BOATMAN, THE**

Before my friend, Peter O'Toole, rode a camel in the desert, he sang this song for me at the Royal Shakespeare Theatre, in Stratford Upon Avon. It had a beginning and an end. I gave it the middle it has now, and I hope, Peter a cara, you approve.

38. **KIMMAGE:**

Described by Brandan as the place where there was made an end to the traditional funeral, they now eat their dead.

39. **LANDLORD AND THE LEPRECHAUN, THE**

A landlord is an animal with two qualities of virtue, both of which have been strained through a loophole in a lawyer's sieve. A leprechaun is a landlord's ideal of the proper height for a tenant.

40. **LEE, THE**

Chief river of County Cork, and badly missed when you're four thousand miles from it on a Saturday night.

41. **LEG, THE**

A walking limb.

42. **LIMERICK RAKE, THE**

A Rake from County Limerick with a Trinity College education in Theology.

43. **LILLI-BULERO:**

Some say it's 'Bail O Dia ar an lila', meaning 'the blessing of God on the lily'. Others have it 'bail oDia ar an leat Ri', meaning 'blessing of God on the half king'. Whoever is wrong there's one thing right, the Irish could well have done without cutting each other up over which of two foreign robbers - James from Scotland or William of Orange - were going to carve them up. Fenians and Orangemen, please take note.

44. **LIVERPOOL LOU:**

A Lonely place, Liverpool, especially during a dock strike. More especially when you see a lonely woman walking down by the lonely Mersey. I never knew anybody of the name - to the immense chagrin of those friends who built up their own romantic pictures of myself in Beatlepool.

45. **LOVE IS TEASING:**

Sometimes.

46. **LOVE OF MY HEART:**

First heard in the Sacra Caor Hotel, Salthill, Galway, half in English, half in Irish. Maybe the proprietor, Eugene Donleavy, knows more about it. I must tell Fintan Connolly to go and ask there sometime.

47. **LONELY DAYS:**

And nights.

48.   MAIDS WHEN YOU'RE YOUNG:

Which came first? There are versions of this song extant all over the British Isles. This one is adapted from the singing of Mrs. Carroll of Rathmines, Dublin.

49   MASTER McGRATH:

The first battle of any real importance the Irish won on English soil.

50   MAN FROM WEXFORD, THE

I first sang this song for Hamish Henderson at the end of the last war. Then he asked me to sing it in Edinburgh, and I was glad I went because I met a lot of decent people like Jeannie Robertson and Jimmie McBeath.

51.   MERRY PLOUGHBOY:

Popular among kids like myself when we were in Fianna - the Young Republican boyscouts - muchly restored by me.

52.   ARKLE: (MIGHTY MILLHOUSE)

Second battle of any real importance the Irish won on English soil.

53.   MO BUACHAILLIN DONN:

Light, but in the rather nice sense.

54   MOUNTJOY HOTEL, THE

A music transcriber working on the tunes used in this book asked, "Say, what's with this hotel commercial?" I explained that it was a little bit of jail satire, Mountjoy being Dublin's Prison. "What a name for a nick!" said Ewan McColl, "It must have been some right twisted bastard thought that one up". This has been extensively re-written from the original by Phil O'Neill.

55.   MR. MURPHY'S TAR-MACADAM HIGHWAYS:

The number of Celtic builders and contractors in Britain must be legion.

56.   MOTHER ENGLAND:

And every word of it true.

57.   MRS. HOOLIGAN'S CHRISTMAS CAKE:

One of the songs used thematically in James Joyce's "Finnegan's Wake". Old music-hall. My Mother and Father used to sing it together when they thought the company was such as would not appreciate National or Traditional songs.

58.   MRS. McHUGH HAS UP AND DIED:

"The real ones I feel sorry for is the ones that is left behind", says he, as he laughed himself sick into a pint of malt whisky.

59.   MURDERER'S DOG, THE

John Martin of Meath whose very special elevating stanza was the last, in part anyway, the first one. I wrote the rest and felt most elevated in the doing.

60. MY BONNY BROWN BOY:

"Lord Randall my so-hu-hun", then they made an 'art' version for "Edward" basso profundo, "my soooon". But up in Belfast they sing, "Where have yeh been all day, Henery me Son? Where have yeh been all day my lover one?" and he says what 'kilt' him was, "Poisoned bea-yens". Then the Cockney one, "Wer did yer lie yer loaf, Enery me son, cor but you ain't arf choked me current bun". The one here was recorded one time by Hamish Henderson with my Mother doing the singing. The only traditional song I know doesn't answer back, without having something rude to say.

61. NEW FREE STATERS, THE

On December 7th, 1922, the Free State forces took Rory O'Connor, Liam Mellowes, Dick McKee and Joe McKelvey from Mountjoy Prison and shot them without warning. DeValera, then on the Republican side, commented that all the might of all the Empires on earth could not have made him do it. On November 12th, 1942, Maurice O'Neill was shot by DeValera's administration in Mountjoy. Patrick McGrath and Thomas Harte were shot by the Dev crowd; Charles Kerins and Richard Goss, George Plant and oh, the list is too, too awful.

62. NO LOVE NO MORE:

Well, well, won't Mr. Freud be surprised!

63. NOT A STAR FROM THE FLAG SHALL FADE:

A really great song about the American Civil War.

64. OH GENTLE YOUTH:

Translated from "Gaelic Songs of the West".

65. OLD ERIN IN THE SEA:

And long may she float there.

66. OUL LEATHER BRITCHES

My Granny English was the same sort of a cook. That's why she was married twice and outlived them both.

67. PATRICK LYNCH'S BOAT:

Gaynor Crist, on whom, Des MacNamara says Michael Donleavy based the characterisation of Dangerfield in his book, "The Ginger Man", loved this song, particularly the bit about, "I'll leave my bones in Santa Cruz, far from my own Mayo". Crist dropped dead in 1964 - in Santa Cruz.

68. PATRIOT GAME, THE

About the death of Feargal O'Hanlon, killed alongside Sean South, on a raid over the Irish border, January 1st, 1957.

69 PAT AND THE GANGERMAN:

The reply of an Irish navvy when he was approached by a foreman who held views which were somewhat apartheid conscious.

70 PAWNSHOP, THE

Attacking the Jews, Hitler declared, "They even infest our society from the lowest of the bottom, the pledge-room! Cast the money changers from the Temple!" The pawnshops of Dublin have old Irish names like Brereton, Kilbride, Davin's and even Finnegan. And they do business just as well in the Christian creed as any other.

71. POEM:

Well, not really, if you put it like that.

72 MY REDHEADED MOT FROM RINGSEND

Raytown, that's what the old people from around Thomcastle Street call Ringsend. My Father's people came from there since they left Wexford in 1259. 'Hobbling' is what most of the people worked at down there years ago. You mean cobbling, surely? I mean h-o-b-b-l-i-n-g, hobbling; the little boat going to take the line of the big boat into the harbour, that's hobbling.

73 RAGMAN'S BALL, THE

A New York film producer friend of mine said he went to Ireland to prove the 'stage.Irishman' a slurring myth invented by slanderers. "Did you find any?" I asked on his return. "Find any!" he exploded, "I found nobody who wasn't one!" I'm not one bit surprised.

74. RIVER SILA, THE

Ewan McColl told me, when I first sang this song in his presence, that it was derived from the ballad of the "Cruel Mother"; well, Ewan, she was a cruel oul bitch right enough.

75. ROCKS OF BAWN, THE

The man who wrote this song didn't die all that long ago. His name was Martin Swiney, and at this moment there is a friend of his, Patrick Quinn, aged ninety, in the old people's home, Cavan. I'm told this man has songs by Swiney which are even better than the "Rocks of Bawn". If he has, they must be great songs altogether.

76. SAINT, THE

My Father has about two versions of this song which deals with the attempt by Kathleen Og of Dara to seduce Saint Kevin of Glendalough. Lovely name, "Gleann Da Lougha', the 'glen of the twin lakes'. The other version he only sings to shock the company.

77. SEA AROUND, THE

I got the line from my Mother which a friend of hers, Mick Byrne, wrote, together with about forty verses he couldn't remember. The line I got was 'Thank God we're surrounded by water', and I thought it far too good to lose.

X

78. **SEAN O'DWYER OF THE GLEN:**

There is considerable confusion existing just now as to the man's actual name. Modern Irish speakers hold it to be 'Sean O'Dubagh a gleanna' = 'Black Sean of the Glen'. Old Irish speakers think it to be 'Dubog' = 'young Dark', but nobody has taken into consideration that the word 'Eir' meant literally 'Heir', which of course gives the song its real point, Sean, Heir to the Glen.

The song is an image of Ireland in the 14th century in the form of an allegory. The goat tied up represents the Clan unable to move. The fallen wood is an allusion to the time the Irish had to seek refuge elsewhere because the English were tearing the forests down to seek them out. The English poet, Spenser, said "I wish that orders were taken for cutting and opening all places through the woods: so that a wide way, of the space of one hundred yards, might be laid open in every of them". This is a translation from the old version sung by the late Donncha O'Maille of Carnock.

79. **SIT YEH DOWN AND I'LL TREAT YEH DECENT:**

Muldoon must have been as well known as Garret Riley or Larry McHales' dog. I first heard this song, or rather bits of it, from a relation of my Father's, my aunt Julia. I next heard the same bits being sung in Paddy and Maureen Donahue's pub in Dublin. I went back the way a bit and wrote the song as you see it now and added a chorus to make it a real drinking song.

80. **SEAN BEAN BOCT, THE**

The poor old woman. The old woman is Ireland, and the song has many sons and daughters. This is one of them.

81. **SLEEP MY LOVE:**

This beautiful lullaby, translated from the Irish, is set to an air people believe was the cradling song for the infant Jesus.

82. **SLIAB NA MBAN:**

The weary Irish. Weary waiting for the French, but never beaten. This is a translation.

83. **SMITH OF BRISTOL:**

Britain ruled the waves but men like the author of "Smith of Bristol" lashed them back into their place with laughter, derisive laughter of course.

84. **SODDING, THE**

Carry on with the coffin, the corps can walk.

85. **SONG FROM THE BACKWOODS:**

The French in Canada are wanting to be on their own and the Irish in Canada are wanting the French to be on their own and will even take up a collection to get them all back to Charlie Doyle. Who's Charlie Doyle, for God's sake? Well, his name is really a Brythonic slur on foreigners who come from abroad into France, Dub Gall, the 'Black Stranger', or 'De Gaulle'.

86. SOUTH DOWN MILITIA, THE

Left Ulster with three hundred and twenty two men to fight the Boers. Were beaten by sixteen Boers' wives and the writer of this particular song.

87. SPINNING WHEEL SONG, THE

Loved by Irish record makers because it's out of copyright.

88. THERE CAME THREE JEWS:

Children's street song of Ireland, England, Scotland, and I wonder if they have any streets in Wales?

89. THREE FARMERS FROM THE NORTH:

Gentleman farmers; raise nothing but their hats.

90. TO DIE FOR IRELAND

Inspired by James Connolly's contention, "Ireland, distinct from her people means nothing to me", and "Patriotism is the last refuge of a scoundrel".

91. TWANGMAN'S REVENGE, THE

The work of M.J. Moran who also had a complete song about Billy Davis, the murderer who had lost both legs and perambulated himself around the city by scudding a bowl with his arms. He would ask for assistance and while being aided he wrapped his arms around the helper and choked him, to rob. Billy the Bowl became afterwards a children's round game.

92. TIP'RARY RECRUIT:

Served him right for saying such things about poor Queen Victoria.

93. TRUST IN DRINK:

Cur preab san ol = put trust in drink. One of the oldest drinking songs in Ireland, very freely translated, cost me nothing, in fact, except the time.

94. WALK MY LOVE:

The women sit home to wait, said O'Casey. They do even yet, while their husbands and boy friends work in England, or America, or anywhere they can get the labour. Twenty five thousand people at least per year leave Ireland and nowadays it is so commonplace that the figure is merely another statistic in the corner of a newspaper.

95 WAXIE'S DARGLE, THE

It was once the annual excursion of the Candlemakers of Dublin to Bray.

96. WEARING OF THE GREEN, THE

Another little trick of Mother England's, imprison a man for respecting his country's National Emblems. Dispossess him if he used the Irish form of his name. Hang him if he objected.

97. WHEN I'M TWENTY:

A song in defence of the age we all love and the young men lucky enough to be living and loving it.

98. YEH MEN OF SWEET LIBERTIES HALLS,

M.J. Moran's song in praise of the Southside of Dublin.

99. YOUNG JOHNNY IS MINE:

Women are vain until they get their eye wiped by another woman and then they behave like ladies, revoltingly.

100. ZOOLOGICAL GARDENS:

The Phoenix Park is one of the best loved and most loved of parks in Europe. In order to get to the Zoo, lovers have to pass the Hollow, and because any-body wanting a good court would be stupid if he passed the Hollow, very few people ever get as far as the Zoo until they are married with children. Because the whole business is of such rare momentum, somebody decided to write a song about it.

Dominic Behan, London, 17th March, 1965.